TALES OF TERROR AND SUSPENSE!

CHAMBER OF CHILLS

No.16

MAR.

CHAMBER OF CHILLS

CHILLS

10¢

THIS WAS AN ETERNAL PATH OF EVIL...THIS WAS A LOATHSOME LABYRINTH OF MADNESS...THIS WAS A...CYCLE OF HORROR

WON'T YOU COME IN?

Does the icy wind bite at you and send chills through your spine? Are you frightened by the ghastly blackness that curdles the winter's air? WELL SHUT THE DOOR AND COME IN.

Come in and read a quartet of terror-filled tales that will wipe the threat of wintry darkness from your mind...You'll have bigger worries!

Come in and read four incredibly different dramas of suspense that bear the famous trademark of CHAMBER OF CHILLS!

Read the fantastic chill-story that unfolds in the CYCLE OF HORROR...a tale that turns through a labyrinth of terror and ends with the most frantic twist!

Read the CURSE OF THE BLACK PANTHER and swirl through a maze of mystery that can only lead to the dead end!

Read the story of THE WAXMAN who dared defy time...and took his chances with a paraf-finish!

And read the daring account of men caught in the endless arms of THE CREEPING DEATH!

So forget the wind, the rain, the hurricanes, the earthquakes and your other troubles. You'll have no time for incidentals in the... CHAMBER OF CHILLS!

"AT LAST"! HE SIGHED. "I'VE ESCAPED"! AND THEN HE SAW THE SHRIVELED BODY, AND THE FEET, AND THE RATS, AND THE DIRT, HE SAW HIS VICTIM AGAIN ...AND AGAIN IN A...

CYCLE of HORROR!

IT WAS THE DEAD OF NIGHT. THE MOON BEAMS TWISTED OMINOUSLY... THE WIND MOANED EERILY THROUGH THE CANYONS OF THE LARGE CITY. A MAN WALKED THE DESERTED STREETS. THE STAGE WAS SET FOR *MURDER*...!

MY FOOTSTEPS SOUND LIKE DRUMBEATS IN THIS *VACUUM* OF AN AVENUE!

CLOP! CLOP! CLOP!

HE WAS ABOUT TO CROSS THE STREET... HE NEVER MADE IT!

ARRRGHHH!!! HELP!!!

N-NO! DON'T!! Y-A-A-A-AH!

THE MAN SANK TO HIS KNEES, THEN FELL DOWN TO HIS DOOM! A QUICK RIFFLING OF HIS POCKETS, AND TWO SHADOWY FIGURES DARTED IN THE ALLEY...

GOT IT! COME ON!!

GASP... GASP...

CLOP!

CLOP! CLOP!

THESE WERE THE MEN... GREG VANTUCCI AND "FINGERS WATSON". FOOTPADS... STICKUP MEN... OF THE MOST DESPERATE KIND. THEY MURDERED WITHOUT THE SLIGHTEST QUALM...

HA! HA...WHAT AN EASY HAUL THIS WUZ, GREG! WE MUSTA GOT ABOUT A COUPLE O'GEES AT LEAST!

I CAN'T WAIT TO COUNT IT!

THEY FINGERED THE BLOOD-MONEY OVER THE TABLE IN THEIR TWO-BIT HIDEOUT. THEN...

IT WAS MY IDEA, FINGERS! I WAS THE ONE WHO KNIFED HIM!

I'LL CROAK HIM RIGHT NOW BEFORE HE CAN TRY ANYTHING

YEAH...BUT I HELD HIM! THE DOUGH'S MINE!...THREE-QUARTERS WORTH! I'LL SHOW YA WHO'S IDEA IT WAS!

I TELL YOU IT'S MINE!

ARGHHH!

I-I-I'LL T-TAKE YOU WITH ME!

UGHHH!

BANG!

HA, HA! SO LONG, JERK! YOUR BULLET ONLY GRAZED ME!

YA LOUSE... YOU DIRTY RAT! I...I'LL BE WAITING! I...ARRGHH!

TOUGH! REAL TOUGH! BUT NOW THE DOUGH'S *MINE!* HA, HA... LET'S GET YOU ON THIS BED, FINGERS! THEN I'LL BURN YOUR CLOTHES SO'S NO ONE CAN RECOGNIZE YOU!

SO LONG, PAL! I'LL LEAVE YA TO THE *RATS!* THAT'S WHAT YOU'RE GOOD FOR ANYWAY! I WON'T BE SEEING YA! HA, HA...

MINUTES AFTERWARDS, GREG VANTUCCI WENT OUT TO A FURIOUS RAINSTORM. THE BULLET BURNED IN HIS STOMACH, AND HE LOOKED AROUND FOR SHELTER...

I'LL TAKE A ROOM IN THAT FLEA-BAG FER THE NIGHT! THEN I'LL MOVE OUT!

BRAAM!

SNAP!

CRACKLE!

GREG FELT SMUG AND SATISFIED. WITH FIVE HUNDRED DOLLARS IN HIS POCKET, HE WAS SITTING ON TOP OF THE WORLD...

HERE YOU ARE, SIR! I HOPE YOU'LL BE PLEASED! IT'S ONE OF OUR BEST ROOMS! IT HAS A *SPECIAL* VIEW!

YEAH! YEAH! CAN THE CHATTER! GIMME THE KEY!

OKAY! NOW TAKE A POWDER! *ULP!! AAGAA!!*

IS SOMETHING THE MATTER, SIR?

K-KEEP THE DOUGH I GAVE YA! I--I'M GETTIN' OUTTA HERE! CHANGED MY MIND!

CLINK!

3

SUDDEN PANIC CLUTCHING AT HIS MIND, GREG VANTUCCI RAN HEADLONG INTO THE STORM-SWEPT STREET AGAIN.

HEY! CABBIE!! OVER *HERE*! HURRY!

I'LL GO TO CLARA'S HOUSE. SHE'S OUTTA TOWN NOW. I GOT THE KEY TO HER APARTMENT!

AND LATER...

OKAY! STOP RIGHT HERE!

WHY DIDN'T I THINK O' THIS BEFORE? JUST GETTING JUMPY FER NOTHING! I MUSTA DOUBLED BACK TO THAT SAME TWO-BIT DUMP! MUSTA BEEN A NEW CLERK AT THAT SHIFT!

GOOD OL' CLARA! I'M SURE GLAD SIS TRAVELS WITH THAT DANCE BAND! THIS APARTMENT IS SURE CONVENIENT! NOW FOR SOME SLEEP!

YA-A-A-AH!

SQUEAK!

SQUEAK!

THE SCREAM WELLED FORTH FROM HIS THROAT IN INVOLUNTARY TERROR HIS MIND WAS PLAYING TRICKS ON HIM! *"FINGERS"* WAS UP THERE! BUT HE COULDN'T BE! THIS WAS THE *OTHER* SIDE OF TOWN!

AIEEE! I--I'M GOING CRAZY! IT'S MY IMAGINATION! I GOTTA GET HOLD O' MYSELF!

I'M TIRED! I NEED A REST! I WANNA SLEEP! THERE'S THE CRANMOR HOTEL...THE BEST IN TOWN! I'M GOING THERE! I GOT THE DOUGH! I'LL SPEND ALL OF IT IF I HAVTA! I JUST *GOTTA* CATCH SOME SHUT-EYE!

HOTEL CRANMOR

RRRRRRRR!

THE MANAGER RANG HIS BELL. THE BELLHOP LOOKED GREG UP AND DOWN WITH SOME DISTASTE BUT THEN SHOWED HIM THE WAY... HE NOTICED GREG'S ROLL OF GREENBACKS...

HERE YOU ARE, SIR! PLEASE STEP INSIDE!

LET 'EM STARE AT ME! WHO CARES HOW I LOOK... AS LONG AS I CAN PAY!

AND THEN... HERE YOU ARE SIR! PLEASE STEP INSIDE!

AAAEEE! THE ROOM! IT'S THAT SAME ROOM!! NO! NO!!

YOU'RE TRYING TO TRICK ME! THIS IS SOME WIERD JOKE! WELL— I WON'T CONFESS! YOU CAN'T MAKE ME! I WANT THIS ROOM INSTEAD!! STAND BACK... OR...OR I'LL KILL YOU!!

SURE! ANYTHING YOU SAY!

AAAAAGHHHHH!!

W-WHAT'S HAPPENING TO ME? WHY DO I KEEP RETURNING TO THIS SAME ROOM? Y-YOU'RE GETTING UP! BUT YOU'RE DEAD! DEAD!!!

YES, GREG! I'AM DEAD! REMEMBER WHAT I SAID? I'LL BE WAITING FOR YOU! HA, HA... DON'T YOU KNOW WHERE YOU ARE?

YOU'RE IN HELL, VANTUCCI! YOU'RE HERE TO SPEND ALL ETERNITY RE-ENACTING THE SCENE OF YOUR CRIME, JUST AS WATSON IS!

YOU SEE, GREG! MY BULLET KILLED YOU! DIDN'T YOU KNOW? HA, HA...

YAAAAAAH!!

THE END

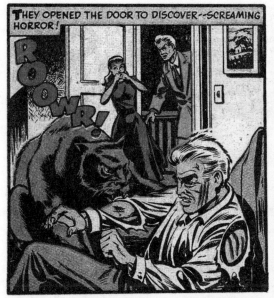

THEY OPENED THE DOOR TO DISCOVER--SCREAMING HORROR!

ROOOWRR!

LENORE--ROBERT--FOR GOD'S SAKES-- WATCH OUT!

IT'S BLOCKED OUR PATH! WE'RE TRAPPED!

ROOWRR

Y-A-A-AH!

LET IT GO, ROBERT! DON'T TRY TO STOP IT! YOU CAN'T, ANYWAY!

RRROWK

WHAT--WHAT WAS THAT THING? IT--LOOKED LIKE A PANTHER--BUT I SWEAR-- IT WAS UNLIKE ANY PANTHER I'VE SEEN!

I--I DON'T KNOW! IT FILLED ME WITH A STRANGE TERROR! OH, ROBERT--DADDY'S HURT!

DON'T MIND ME, MY CHILD! COUGH-COUGH! I'M AN OLD MAN ANYWAY--I--I DIDN'T EXPECT TO LIVE THIS LONG. I--I'VE BEEN FORTUNATE! COUGH... COUGH...

DARLING--HE DOESN'T LOOK SO GOOD! STAY WITH HIM! THE PHONE HAS BEEN RIPPED OUT IN THE STRUGGLE! I'M CALLING THE POLICE AND A DOCTOR!

DADDY--DADDY--WHY AM I SHAKING THIS WAY? I--I'VE NEVER BEEN LIKE OTHER GIRLS ...I'VE NEVER BEEN AFRAID OF ANYTHING IN MY LIFE-- NOW THIS! WHAT WAS IT? WHAT HAS IT DONE TO YOU? SOB....SOB...

LISTEN CLOSELY, DEAR... I--I'M DYING...I'M NOT YOUR FATHER! I MUST TELL YOU THE TRUTH NOW...

3

"THEY TOOK ME INSIDE AND PROCEEDED TO BRING ME BACK TO HEALTH! DAYS MUST HAVE PASSED--FOR I KNEW NOT THE DIFFERENCE. BUT GRADUALLY, I BECAME AWARE OF MY SURROUNDINGS. ALL THROUGH MY CONVALESCENCE ONE OF THEM WAS ALWAYS BY MY SIDE..."

"THEN, ONE DAY, I DECIDED TO FIND OUT WHERE I WAS..."

--BUT WHERE AM I? HOW COME YOU SPEAK ENGLISH?

YOU ARE DEEP WITHIN THE GROTTO OF WHAT YOU CALL "GRAND CANYON"! WE ARE THE PANTHER PEOPLE--AND KILL ALL OUTSIDERS-- BUT SHARLAL AND I HAVE SPARED YOU YOUR LIFE FOR A REASON!

--INCREDIBLE--YET HERE YOU ARE RIGHT BEFORE MY EYES! BUT WHAT IS THE REASON THAT YOU'VE SPARED ME?

UNDERSTAND FIRST THAT WE ARE NOT AS YOU! WE ARE-- DIFFERENT! PERHAPS OUR GREAT ANCESTORS WERE AS YOU--BUT CERTAIN CHEMICALS HERE HAVE CHANGED US TO CREATURES OF THE NIGHT!

THERE--IS THE MASTER WE SERVE! THE FULL MOON! WHEN MIDNIGHT APPROACHES, WE TURN INTO BEASTS! IT IS THIS TIME OF THE SEASON WHERE YOU MUST NOW BE PROTECTED EVEN FROM US-- FOR WE WILL TEAR YOU TO PIECES IN OUR ALTERED FORM!

I--I CAN HARDLY BELIEVE ALL THIS!

"BUT BELIEVE IT, I HAD TO! SHARLAL AND HER MATE HAD MADE A CAGE LARGE ENOUGH FOR ME TO GET INTO WHEN THEIR TRANSFORMATION APPROACHED THEM. NOTHING COULD REACH THE CAGE FROM THE GROUND..."

GREAT SCOTT! T-THEY'RE CHANGING! AAAAAAGHH-- THEY'RE CHANGING!

ONE SLASH OF THEIR CLAWS--AND I'LL BE RIPPED TO PIECES! GOOD LORD--THESE ARE SUPERNATURAL BEINGS! BUT WHY DO THEY WANT TO KEEP ME ALIVE? WHY...?

4

"I NEVER FOUND OUT UNTIL, ONE DAY, AN EARTHQUAKE SHOOK OUR SMALL ROCK-HUT. THEN SHARLAL'S MATE TOLD ME...."

OUR LEADER, XARLAK--PLANS TO TAKE US TO THE SURFACE WORLD! BUT WE KNOW THAT XARLAK IS EVIL! HE MEANS US HARM--WE HAVE NO DESIRE TO KILL--ONLY WHEN WE CHANGE...

--AND THE BABY--?

YOU WILL TAKE OUR DAUGHTER BACK WITH YOU TO YOUR WORLD, WHEN THE UNDERGROUND GOD STRIKES AGAIN, BRINGING THE ROCKS DOWN UPON US--FOR XARLAK PLANS CONQUEST--AND WE DO NOT AGREE! HE IS EVIL--WICKED--EVIL--WICKED!

"EVIL--WICKED--EVIL--HOW THOSE WORDS REMAINED IN MY MIND, THROUGH THE MANY TERRIBLE DAYS THAT FOLLOWED. ALWAYS WITH THE FULL-MOON THEY WOULD CHANGE AND TRY TO KILL ME--AND I WAS TERRIFIED. FOR THEY WOULD SUCCEED EVENTUALLY...

EVIL--WICKED-- EVIL--HA, HA... ROOWWRRR...

NO--NO! NO!

"THEN ONE DAY--THE INEVITABLE HAPPENED! THE OTHERS FOUND OUT ABOUT ME--I HAD TAKEN MY USUAL REFUGE IN MY CAVE, WHEN THE EARTHQUAKE BEGAN..."

THEY'RE FIGHTING AMONG THEMSELVES NOW! THEY'LL BE CRUSHED UNDER THOSE ROCKS!

RRUMBLE!

ROOWWRRR

"I WATCHED THE ROCKS FALLING ON THEM, CRUSHING, TEARING, KILLING THEM...THEN MY OWN CAGE WAS CAUGHT IN THE MAELSTROM OF NATURE...I KNEW NO MORE...."

OHHHH...

BARRRAMM!

"AND WHEN I CAME TO..."

SHARLAL--LET ME HELP! YOUR BABY IS STILL ALIVE!

TAKE HER AND GO! THERE IS THE PASSAGE-WAY! GO QUICKLY--WE ARE DOOMED! DOOMED!

"HOURS OF FANTASTIC, INCREDIBLE, TERRIBLE ADVENTURES LATER, I REACHED THE OUTER WORLD...."

ALL I HAVE TO DO IS FOLLOW THAT RIDGE--AND I'LL BE SAFE, SHE SAID. WE MADE IT, LITTLE ONE... BUT WE AREN'T ALONE...

5

"NO--WE WEREN'T ALONE--FOR OUT OF THAT TERRIBLE CATASTROPHE HAD ALSO SURVIVED XARLAK--LEADER OF THE RACE! HE WAS LARGER AND BLACKER THAN ALL THE REST! I HAD RECOGNIZED HIM IN THE GLOOM... NOW BEGAN YEARS OF RUNNING FOR US!"

BUT, DADDY-- WHY DO WE HAVE TO LEAVE? I LIKE IT HERE!

DO AS I SAY, LENORE!

"FOR ALWAYS XARLAK PURSUED US-- WANTING TO RECLAIM LENORE! HE WAS THE LAST OF HIS RACE-- AND SHE HAD TO BE HIS MATE! BUT I HAD GIVEN MY PLEDGE TO PROTECT HER... AND SO THE YEARS PASSED..."

ISN'T IT BEAUTIFUL TONIGHT, DADDY! THE FULL MOON THRILLS ME SO!

YES... SHE HASN'T RECEIVED THE CURSE YET! "AT TWENTY-ONE, IT WILL COME ON HER"... MAY I NEVER SEE THAT DAY!

--AND THAT IS MY CONFESSION! BEWARE, LENORE-- BEWARE OF FULL MOON! OH, MY DEAR-- MY DEAR... COUGH... COUGHH... GOODBYE...

NO! NO! DON'T LEAVE ME!

HE'S DEAD, ROBERT! HE'S DEAD!

BUT YOU'RE NOT ALONE, DARLING! YOU STILL HAVE ME! YOU'RE COMING TO LIVE WITH MOTHER, FATHER AND ME AT OUR HOME!

SO LENORE DID JUST THAT. BUT NOW A STRANGE REST-LESSNESS ATE AT HER VITALS. SHE HAD JUST PASSED TWENTY-ONE. AND SHE HAD NEVER QUITE FORGOTTEN HER FOSTER-FATHER'S DYING CONFESSION...

WHAT'S WRONG, ARLING?

OH-- HOW CAN I MAKE HIM UNDERSTAND? HOW?

LENORE MANAGED TO HIDE HER SECRET FOR A FEW MORE DAYS. THEN ONE AFTERNOON, SHE, ROBERT, AND SOME FRIENDS HAD BEEN DELAYED ON A HUNT. NIGHT APPROACHED...

PLEASE TAKE ME HOME, ROBERT! PLEASE! SOMETHING IS WRONG WITH ME! I--I FEEL STRANGE...

ALL RIGHT, HONEY! IT'S LATE ANYWAY! SO LONG, FOLKS! SEE YOU LATER!

FASTER—FASTER SHE RAN, TRYING TO RESIST THE STRANGE CURSE WITHIN HERSELF! BUT THE HOUR OF CHANGE WAS AT HAND--AND NOTHING COULD STOP DESTINY!

LENORE! WHAT'S HAPPENING TO YOU? OHHH--YOU'RE CHANGING-- CHANGING!

DON'T LOOK AT ME--HURRY HOME, ROBERT! PLEASE, DARLING-- HURRY HOME!

NOW THE BEYOND TOOK DOMINANCE OF THE GIRL THAT HAD ONCE BEEN LENORE! THE BLACK PANTHER STALKED ITS PREY ONCE MORE--THIS TERRORIZED MAN WHO HAD BEEN HER SWEETHEART.

LENORE! I--I'M GOING MAD!! DARLING--IT'S ME...DON'T YOU RECOGNIZE ME? OHHH...

RROWWRR

BUT DESTINY ALSO PLAYS STRANGE JOKES--FOR JUMPING OUT OF THE UNDERBRUSH CAME XARLAK!

Y-A-A-A-AH!

RROWWRR!

DO NOT TOUCH HIM, LENORE! I SHALL KILL TONIGHT! WE WILL GLORY IN OUR KILL TOGETHER --YOU AND I! WE SHALL START A NEW RACE! HA, HA.... I HAVE WAITED LONG FOR THIS MOMENT!

ROOWWRWRWR!

AIIEEE!

OVER AND OVER THE TWO GREAT BEASTS ROLLED, LOCKED IN A DEATH-STRUGGLE. THEN WHEN IT WAS ALL OVER, ROBERT CRAWLED OVER TO LENORE...

RROWRRR
PFFRTITT PSSSTTPFFFTT!

IT'S OVER, DARLING! I --SAVED YOU! I TOLD YOU MY LOVE WAS STRONGER THAN LIFE! GOOD-BYE...

NO, DON'T DIE! COME BACK TO ME, LENORE! LENORE! LENORE! LENORE! OH, MY DARLING-- NEVERMORE!!

BUT, BLOOD CANNOT BE ERASED! A YOUNG MAN'S SCREAMS SHRILLED INTO THE NIGHT FOR HIS SWEETHEART--BROKEN, SOBBING, CRAZED--FOR HE TOO HAD REALIZED THAT THE CURSE OF THE BLACK PANTHER WAS ENDED! The End

WHAT AGE WOULD YOU LIKE TO REACH? 100? 200? 300? BETTER NOT SET YOUR MARK TOO HIGH TILL YOU READ THE GRUESOME TALE OF—

THE WAX MAN!

IT WAS 300 YEARS AGO, AND CALEB WAINRIGHT WAS PROWLING THROUGH THE HOME OF BENJAMIN WHITTAKER, RENOWNED COLONIAL SCIENTIST—

SHOULD BE GOOD PICKINGS HERE! HEAVY PEWTER PLATES—SILVER CANDLESTICKS—

SUDDENLY—

WHO'S THERE?

THE OLD FOOL HAS A FIERY TEMPER! HE'S SURE TO LET GO WITH THAT MUSKET IF HE SEES ME! I'LL HIDE HERE 'TILL HE PASSES, AND THEN—

AGGHEHH!

KRASH

IT'S A HANGING MATTER IF THEY GET ME NOW! BETTER LEAVE FAST--THROUGH THE WINDOW OF HIS WORK ROOM! IT OPENS TOWARD THE REAR OF THE HOUSE!

BUT WHAT'S THIS? ELIXIR OF LIFE?

ELIXIR OF LIFE
AND I TRULY BELIEVE THAT IF ONE QUAFFS THIS LIQUID HE

"HE WILL LIVE TO BE AT LEAST FIVE HUNDRED YEARS. AND YET I AM AFRAID TO TRY IT--"

WELL, I'M NOT AFRAID!

WHAT HAVE I GOT TO LOSE? WHY SHOULD ANYONE BE AFRAID TO LIVE FIVE HUNDRED YEARS?

YES, CALEB DRANK DEEP-- AND SOME FIFTY YEARS LATER--

HEH! HEH! I LOOK MY AGE--BUT I FEEL SPRY AS A YOUNKER! WHO CARES WHAT I LOOK LIKE--AS LONG AS I FEEL YOUNG!

2

CALEB DIDN'T CARE BUT DID YOU EVER SEE A MAN 150 YEARS OLD?

TWO HUNDRED YEARS OLD?

OR THREE HUNDRED YEARS OLD?

YES, CALEB WAS A RANK, FOUL THING OF HORROR-- AND AS HE PASSED THROUGH THE STREETS--

EEEEE

THE TOWNSPEOPLE WERE HORRIFIED AND DECIDED TO TAKE ACTION--

HE'LL FRIGHTEN SOMEONE TO DEATH ONE OF THESE DAYS--ONLY ONE THING TO DO--INFORM THE AUTHORITIES AND LOCK HIM UP!

I DON'T WANT TO BE LOCKED UP! I STILL HAVE TWO HUNDRED YEARS OF LIFE AHEAD OF ME! I'M YOUNG-- YOUNG--YOUNGER THAN ANYONE-- DESPITE MY ANCIENT SHAPE!

THE WAX WORKS! I'LL HIDE IN THERE 'TILL--NO--WAIT--I'VE A BETTER IDEA-- A WONDERFUL IDEA--

CHANDLER WAX WORKS

3

CHANDLER MAKES THESE WAX FIGURES HIMSELF--HE LIVES UP UPSTAIRS--IF CAN GET HIM TO--HEH! HEH! I'LL BE SAFE THEN!

MOMENTS LATER--

AGHH! *YOU!* WHAT DO YOU WANT!

I WANT YOU TO COVER MY MOULDERING FLESH WITH WAX--MAKE ME LOOK YOUNG--HANDSOME--AS YOUNG AS I FEEL!

YES--YES--ANYTHING! BUT PUT THAT KNIFE AWAY!

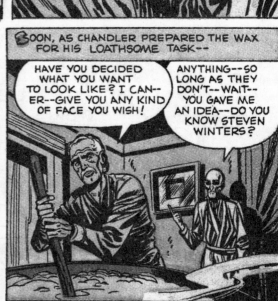

SOON, AS CHANDLER PREPARED THE WAX FOR HIS LOATHSOME TASK--

HAVE YOU DECIDED WHAT YOU WANT TO LOOK LIKE? I CAN--ER--GIVE YOU ANY KIND OF FACE YOU WISH!

ANYTHING--SO LONG AS THEY DON'T--WAIT--YOU GAVE ME AN IDEA--DO YOU KNOW STEVEN WINTERS?

YES, OF COURSE--THE WEALTHIEST MAN IN TOWN! BUT WHY--?

YOU'LL MAKE ME LOOK LIKE HIM! EXACTLY LIKE HIM!

FINE! FINE! IT GLISTENS LIKE REAL, HEALTHY FLESH! THEY'LL NEVER KNOW THE DIFFERENCE!

AND THEN THE REST OF THE BODY--

AND FINALLY--

THERE-- FINISHED!

YES--EXCEPT FOR ONE LITTLE DETAIL--

I CAN'T AFFORD TO HAVE A LIVING SOUL KNOW OF THIS CHANGE! SO--AHH--THE WAX IS FIRM AND STRONG-- MY FINGERS ARE SUPPLE AND NEW!

AGHHH

SOME DAYS LATER--

WINTERS FREQUENTLY PASSES HERE ON LONELY WALKS! I'LL WAIT-- I HAVE PLENTY OF TIME, MORE THAN ANYONE ELSE!

PRESENTLY, WINTER'S PASSED, AND CALEBS NEW WAXEN FINGERS REACHED OUT AND CLUTCHED WARM, LIVING FLESH!

I'LL DISPOSE OF THE BODY IN THE SWAMP--WHERE IT WILL NEVER BE FOUND AGAIN! AND THEN I'LL BE WINTER'S WITH ALL HIS WEALTH!

LATER THAT AFTERNOON--

FINE! THEY DIDN'T NOTICE THE DIFFERENCE AT ALL!

HOW PALE THE MASTER LOOKS! I HOPE HE ISN'T ILL!

AND THAT EVENING AS CALEB LAY IN WINTER'S BED--

I'LL LIVE HERE FOR A WHILE--THEN DISAPPEAR WITH ALL THE MONEY I CAN LAY MY HANDS ON! ANOTHER WORKER IN WAX CAN GIVE ME AN ENTIRELY NEW FACE!

CALEB SLEPT WELL THAT NIGHT, AND NEXT MORNING WHILE HE WAS STILL ASLEEP--

STRANGE HABIT OF THE MASTER'S-- STARTING EACH DAY WITH A STEAM BATH!

IT MUST MEAN A LOT TO HIM--SINCE HE'S HAD THE MECHANISM SPECIALLY BUILT INSIDE HIS BEDROOM!

THIS HEAT--IT--IT'S HORRIBLE! MELTING THE WAX! MUST STOP IT! MUST GET OUT!

AGHHH! HELP! THE WAX--IT'S HOT-- BURNING ME ALIVE! HELP!

AND WHEN THE SERVANTS ENTERED THE ROOM--

THE MASTER-- LOOK--AGHHH!

THE END

THE MAN

The car was smashed to a twisted steel pulp, and yet he was alive.

But look -- what's that?

A young man, smashed, bloody, you couldn't even tell who he was -- and very much dead! Could he have killed him? Was it a car -- his car -- that did it? But, wait...first of all...

WHO WAS HE?

"Yeah," he asked himself, "just who am I? I don't remember how I even got here! I-I-I can't remember a thing!"

He reached into his pocket...

"No wallet...no identification...no money...nothing but a simple handkerchief!"

Suddenly there were voices coming over the road!

And now there were the people... lots of people...an endless line of people...a mob of people!

"Hey," he called. "Help me!"

"We hear you, bud!" said one of the men in front. "We hear you, and we see you."

The man came up to him...

SLAMMM!

"Oww! Why did you hit me?"

"What do you think we are -- fools! Grab him, men!"

SLAMMMM!

"Stop it! Leave me alone! Where am I?"

"Where do you think you are, in Tokyo? Listen, mister, we don't know who you are and that's not important. We know what you did!"

"What I did? I don't understand you"

"Enough of this," said a man. "Let's get this lynching over with!"

"Lynching?" he cried. "Lynch me for what?"

Little bubbles of perspiration poured down his face in a trail of panic. His eyes bulged frantically...his body twisted inside him! "tell me! Tell me! What have I done?"

"Look at what you did to him! Look at him lying over there!"

"I-I-I don't even know him! I don't even know who I am, I tell you! It's all a horrible mystery!" His words were tumbling over themselves in a frantic plea for mercy...for knowledge. "Don't I even get a trial?"

"A trial? Did you give him a trial? No! You were out to murder him and you did! He told us someone was out to get him...that he had to get out of town! But you beat him to a punch! But one of the kids saw the whole scene, and he ran back to town! You're licked, mister, so face it -- and talk!"

"I tell you it's all new to me...I don't remember a thing..."

"Enough of this talk! String him up!"

It was too late...hands were at work...the rope was on the tree...and now around his neck!

"No! Stop it! I remember now...it wasn't me...I can explain it all...Aeee!

It was too late for explanations...it was all over...but a young boy was talking...

"Pop, that didn't look like the man. I'm sure that's not the guy I saw!"

THE EXCITED SCIENTISTS LOST NO TIME! THE KEY TWISTED A TURN OF TERROR IN THE RUSTY LOCK AND SLOWLY THE HUGE DOOR SWUNG OPEN TO REVEAL...

IT--IT'S HORRIBLE! JUST THE SIGHT OF IT FRIGHTENS ME!

NO! THIS IS THE GUARDIAN OF THE CITY, GENTLEMEN! THIS HORROR STOOD AS A BASTION AGAINST THE FOES OF UR IN ANCIENT TIMES!

THEN WE ARE ON THE VERY THRESHOLD OF A CIVILIZATION THAT HAS BEEN THOUGHT A MYTH!

YES! WE MUST TRANSPOSE THIS BLOCK TO OUR SHIP AT ONCE! AS SOON AS THE WORLD GIVES US THE PROPER RECOGNITION, WE'LL BE BACK TO INVESTIGATE THIS PLACE FURTHER!

THUS, THE OMINOUS-LOOKING SLAB OF STONE WAS CARTED TO THE DOCK AND PLACED ON BOARD...

I STILL THINK WE'RE MAKING A MISTAKE, RAND! IT--IT'S NOT RIGHT SOMEHOW-- TO DISTURB ITS RESTING-PLACE!

NONSENSE, CARTWRIGHT! NOW DO AS I SAY! WE CAN'T WASTE TOO MUCH TIME!

THE JOURNEY BACK TO AMERICA WAS NOW IN ITS SECOND DAY. HANS CARTWRIGHT HAD BEEN UNCOMFORT-ABLE EVER SINCE THE BLOCK WAS PUT ON BOARD...

UMMMPHHH... I MUST SLEEP... I KEEP THINKING ABOUT THAT HORRIBLE CREATURE... I...

YAAAAAAHH

W-WHAT WAS THAT?

SOUNDS LIKE CARTWRIGHT! HE WENT TO BED EARLY TONIGHT-- WASN'T FEELING TOO WELL!

YAAAAAAA

COME ON! THE MAN MUST BE IN MORTAL TERROR! I HEAR SOMETHING THRASHING ABOUT INSIDE!

HIS CABIN IS THE ONE ON THE LEFT! CAREFUL!

CARTWRIGHT--ARE YOU--GOOD LORD!

AAAAAGHH--THE MONSTER OF THE SLAB!

ZZZZZZZZZ

QUICK! GRAB THIS-- THIS THING--WHAT-EVER IT IS!

IT'S SLITHERING OUT THROUGH THE PORT-HOLE! CALL THE CAPTAIN AND THE CREW!

HOW HAD THE MONSTER COME TO LIFE? WHAT WAS IT? WHERE WAS IT? THESE WERE THE QUESTIONS THAT WHIRRED THROUGH THE HEADS OF THE GRIM MEN.

BE ON GUARD, ALL OF YOU! IF WHAT YOU SAY IS TRUE-- THEN WE'RE DEALING WITH A MENACE OF UNKNOWN POWER!

I--I CAN'T BELIEVE THIS COULD BE ACTUALLY HAPPENING!

LOOK! GREAT SCOTT! LOOK!

3

IT WON'T DIE! I'VE HIT IT AT LEAST A DOZEN TIMES--*AND IT WON'T DIE!* YAAAAH!

LOOK! WE'RE SURROUNDED ON ALL SIDES BY THOSE TENTACLES! AND--THAT--THAT CREATURE IS GROWING!

THERE'S A LIFE-BOAT OVER HERE! IT'S OUR ONLY CHANCE!

AAAAAGH! ITS TENTACLES HAVE ME BY THE THROAT! AAAAAGHH--URRRGHHH...

ALL HANDS PREPARE TO ABANDON SHIP!

HURRY--HURRY! IT'S GROWING TO FANTASTIC PROPORTIONS! HERE--GIVE ME THAT DYNAMITE STICK!

BUT NOW THE ENTIRE SHIP WAS DWARFED BY THE RAPIDLY-GROWING HORROR! SWIFTLY, IT SENT OUT ITS TENTACLES, GROPING, POKING INTO CREVICES, SWINGING BACK AND FORTH IN AN ENDLESS LUST FOR LIFE!

ROW, MEN! *ROW!* THE SHIP IS SINKING FROM THAT BLOATED WEIGHT! THE SUCTION WILL DRAG US ALL DOWN IF WE DON'T GET CLEAR!

HERE GOES NOTHING! IF IT DOESN'T EXPLODE, WE'RE FINISHED!

SWISHH

YOU DID IT, JAMES! YOU'VE DESTROYED THE MONSTER!

I WONDER! THE LEGEND SAID IT WAS INDESTRUCTIBLE! BUT NOW LET IT REST UNDER MILES OF WATER...CAPTAIN-- WE MUST NEVER SPEAK ABOUT THIS EXPERIENCE TO ANYONE! THE WORLD WOULD LAUGH AT US!

BARRRROOOOMM

AMEN! LET IT BE FORGOTTEN AS IT WAS MEANT TO BE!

THE END

5

NEW FIGURE MOLD
French WAIST

ONLY 2.48

FEATURES *Galore*
Streamline Waistline. Hide Bulges. Adjustable. Washable. Made of satin and 2 way stretch. Fully guaranteed. Light weight. Cool. Will not rumple or ride up. Sizes 20 to 44.

FEATURES STREAM-LINE WAISTLINE HIDE BULGES

No more tummy bulge and clumsy waistline! Instead ENJOY a lovely, shapely "middle" — the most important part of your figure. Just slip FRENCH WAIST caressingly around you. Presto-chango, like magic you have graceful alluring curves. Unwanted bulges are molded to the most flattering curves . . . sit, bend, walk and dance with comfortable even grace.

ADJUSTABLE TO TAILOR-MADE FIT

The amazing satin laced front puts in your hands the power to mold your figure to a new loveliness. Gives you that vibrant, appealing effect of the slim youthful waist — the secret of glamorous women who want to look thin and stylish. You've never enjoyed so much freedom, comfort and style in anything you've worn. The 4 extra length detachable and adjustable garters completes FRENCH WAIST.

Look Lovely in French Waist

This Beautiful Model shows you how you can look in "French Waist." Our taffeta butterfly dress flatters every figure. Figure-magic for every woman — no matter her size! The sophisticated drape, the elegant cut, the face-framing neckline are eternally feminine, eternally enchanting! In rustling rayon taffeta in navy, black, peacock.

STYLE NO. 45493

Sizes 9-17, 10-20		$10.98
Sizes 40-48, 20½-28½		$11.98

10 DAY TRIAL FREE

Order today. Wear 10 days FREE. If not delighted return for refund. Waist sizes 20 to 44, $2.48. (50¢ additional for the 4 extra-length detachable and adjustable garters.)

FREE TRIAL COUPON

GUARANTEED DISTRIBUTORS CO. Dept. F868
836 Broadway, New York 3, N. Y.

Rush my new FRENCH WAIST three-in-one at once. If I am not thrillingly satisfied I will return it after 10-day FREE trial for prompt refund of full purchase price.

Size .... (waist size in inches.)

Also send .... sets of extra-length detachable and adjustable garters at only 50¢ for set of four.

☐ Send C.O.D. I will pay postman on delivery plus few cents postage.

☐ I enclose payment. The Guaranteed Distributors Co. will pay postage.

NAME...

ADDRESS..

Style No. 9811—Our 3 piece "VERSATILE WONDER SUIT." Wonderful washable butcher rayon linen. Smart one button link. Red jacket with slim navy skirt and clever detachable white tattersall check dickey accented with three small pearlized buttons.

Sizes: 9-17
10-18
10⁹⁸
Sizes: 14½-22½
11.98

Style No. 4398—Our 6 ply ribbed bengaline faille all purpose "DUSTER COAT," beautifully tailored, full flare, slash pockets, little turn-up collar, ¾ cuff sleeves, all finished seams. Navy, black, red, champagne.

Sizes: 9-19
10-20
10⁹⁸
Sizes: 14½-22½
11.98

Style No. 4355—Our "COAT-DRESS." Everything you want to take you out elegantly and to the best places. Fly-away collar 'n cuffs. Comfortable batwing sleeves that fit easily over other dresses and jackets and pocket-proud skirt fullness. Rhinestone studded belt. Cotton and rayon faille. Black, navy, red and beige.

Sizes: 9-17
10-20
10⁸⁹

CHAMBER OF CHILLS MAGAZINE, MAY, 1953, Vol. 1, No. 17, IS PUBLISHED BI-MONTHLY by WITCHES TALES, INC., 1860 Broadway, New York 23, N.Y. Entered as second class matter at the Post Office at New York, N.Y under the Act of March 3, 1879. Single copies 10c. Subscription rates, 10 issues for $1.00 in the U.S. and possessions, elsewhere $1.50. All names in this periodical are entirely fictitious and no identification with actual persons is intended. Contents copyrighted, 1953, by Witches Tales, Inc., New York City. Printed in the U.S.A.

THE INNER CIRCLE

Enter the INNER CIRCLE, the last step before the CHAMBER OF CHILLS. Here is where you learn of what waits you... here is where you can give us your comments.

We use the INNER CIRCLE as much as you do. For here is where we present our case. Here is where we try to show you what we're doing, what we're planning. And here is where we get our verdict!

We have ideas -- big ideas, important ideas. But they've got to be tested, they've got to be proven. We feel that the INNER CIRCLE will give us our answer.

This month, we're featuring four amazingly different type of stories. Each with a different kick, each with a different meaning. And we want to know what YOU think of them... how YOU rate them!

Which one is YOUR favorite? Is there one we should have thrown out? What type of story would YOU like to see more of?

Is AMNESIA something to remember? Has the BIG FIGHT got that big punch? Is THE COLLECTOR worth keeping? Is the BRIDGE worth crossing?

* * * *

Let us know. Drop us a post card, pen a letter, and send to:

THE INNER CIRCLE
CHAMBER OF CHILLS
1860 Broadway
New York 23, N. Y.

CHAMBER OF CHILLS

Contents NO. 17

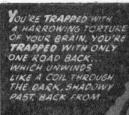

YOU'RE *TRAPPED* WITH A *HARROWING TORTURE* OF YOUR *BRAIN*. YOU'RE *TRAPPED* WITH ONLY *ONE ROAD BACK*... WHICH *UNWINDS* LIKE A COIL THROUGH THE *DARK*, *SHADOWY PAST*, BACK FROM...

AMNESIA!

YOU WALK A QUIET ROAD, A DEATH-LIKE ROAD...

YOUR STEADY STEPS CARRY YOU THROUGH THE RAIN THAT FALLS IN A HEAVY, DRONING TATTOO OF WATER...

BUT SUDDENLY...A JAGGED BOLT OF LIGHTNING STRIKES!

YAAAAH!

You don't know what happened next and you don't hear the blaring wail of an ambulance's siren...

STRUCK BY LIGHTNING! IT'S A GOOD THING WE GOT THERE WHEN WE DID!

YEAH, BUT WE BETTER GET HIM TO THE HOSPITAL... FAST!

And then you hear...then you see...

WHAT HAPPENED...?

YOU WERE HIT BY LIGHTNING. WE FOUND YOU BY THE CEMETERY!

YES. YOU'RE LUCKY TO BE ALIVE, MR... MR...? BY THE WAY, WHAT IS YOUR NAME?

You beat at your brain...you search through your mind...

WHY I'M...I'M... I CAN'T REMEMBER MY NAME! I...I DON'T KNOW WHO I AM!

HMMM! AMNESIA.

PROBABLY. AFTER THAT BLOW ANYTHING MIGHT HAVE HAPPENED. STRANGE...HOW HE LIVED THROUGH IT!

Amnesia! Something you think only others will have...but never YOURSELF! This torment has captured YOU! It surrounds you. It has taken root and it grows!

I'VE GOT TO FIND OUT WHO I AM! AND I CAN'T DO IT IN THIS ROOM!

THE DOCTORS SAID THEY FOUND ME BY THE CEMETERY. MAYBE... I CAN FIND A CLUE TO MY IDENTITY THERE!

You go back to the cemetery, you scan the muddy earth before you...groping, searching for a clue that might mean remembrance...

GOT TO FIND SOMETHING... ANYTHING. WAIT! WHAT'S THAT?

2

3

THEN, WITH A FEAR-STRICKEN, NUMBING EXPECTANCY, YOU ENTER, AND BLACKNESS RANK WITH THE QUIET OF DEATH CONFRONTS YOU...

EVERYTHING'S SO *OLD!* WHAT DOES IT MEAN? *WHERE AM I?*

YOU DELVE DEEPER INTO THE AGED, FETID DILAPIDATION... AND YOU'RE STILL UNAWARE OF A SINISTER BEING THAT WATCHES...

GAD, WHAT A PLACE! THIS STAIRCASE... SOMEONE'S HERE...

THEN SUDDENLY YOU TURN...

YOU HAVE *RETURNED!* WHAT TOOK YOU SO LONG?

YOUR HEART BEATS WILDLY... CHILLS ICE YOUR SPINE!

RETURNED? WHA...WHAT DO YOU MEAN?

DON'T PLAY GAMES! COME, THE OTHERS ARE WAITING!

YOU DUCK, YOU RUN...YOU'RE *FEARFUL* OF YOUR *PAST!* WHAT DOES THIS ALL MEAN?

WHAT ARE YOU AFRAID OF?

NOOO! RUN! GOT TO GET AWAY! THESE STAIRS...

COME BACK. DO NOT RUN!

IT'S FOLLOWING ME! GOT TO GET TO THAT DOOR... GOT TO...

4

MADE IT. NOW...

YES, YOU MADE IT, DIDN'T YOU? YOU'VE COME TO THE OTHER SIDE OF THE DOOR...

I...NO! NOOO!

HE'S HERE!

IT'S ABOUT TIME!

THEY COME CLOSER...THEY LOOM ABOVE YOU...AND YOUR QUEST FOR MEMORY IS REPLACED BY *FEAR!*

WE HAVE BEEN WAITING...

...FOR YOU! HA, HA, HA!

KEEP AWAY!!

THEY GRAB YOU...AND THEIR TOUCH FEELS LIKE THE STING OF DEATH! THEY LEAD YOU TO A CHAIR...

DON'T... DON'T....

WE WON'T HARM YOU. WE CAN'T! WE KNOW WHO YOU ARE!

HA, HA! THEY KNOW...BUT DO *YOU?*

SIT DOWN.

BUT *I* DON'T! TELL ME... WHO AM I?

STOP JOKING, YOU...

...*DEVIL,* YOU!

NOW...I KNOW! HA HA HA HA!

5

COLD TYPE

The Clarion was the greatest newspaper in the world. Everyone knew it. Everyone said it. And perhaps there was no man who knew it and said it more than Cecil Aldrich.

"Guess there's going to be a depression," he'd say to Mrs. Aldrich.

"Why?" she'd ask.

"Why?" He'd laugh back at her. "Because it says so right here in the Clarion. And you know darn well, darling, if the Clarion's got it, it's going to be true!"

Then at another time he'd say, "Well, I guess there really is a crime wave in the city."

And Mrs. Aldrich would say, "But... but..."

"No but's about it!" Mr. Aldrich would answer. "Sure I know that the Enquirer and the Daily Call and the other scandal sheets have been screaming it for months. Then it was boloney. But now, look! It's in the Clarion."

Yes, it was in the Clarion, and it had to be true. The black cold type of the greatest newspaper in the world always read the truth.

Then one morning, a morning no different from any other morning, Cecil Aldrich kissed his wife good-bye in the doorway, promised he'd be home early from the office and began marching down the street.

He reached the corner, handed the newsboy a nickel and folded a Clarion under his arm-pit. He waited a few seconds for the bus, walked into it and took a seat next to the window.

He leafed through the first pages of the greatest newspaper in the world, and then suddenly his heart stopped beating...

"N-n-no!" His eyes couldn't believe what they saw. But there it was in the black, unimpeachable, cold type of the Clarion:

"EXECUTIVE COMMITS SUICIDE

"Cecil Aldrich, vice-president of the Corner Drug Company, killed himself early today by slashing his wrists with a razor blade. There was no apparent reason for the suicide. The body was found..."

He couldn't read on. His mind swirled with a rush of horror and his eyes saw nothing but black, blurred, cold type!

"But, it's impossible," he told himself. "Th-they've finally made a mistake. It's another man, that's what it is!"

Then he stopped talking to himself. Then he stopped thinking. Then the bus stopped and he got up. He walked to the exit door, and it opened. He walked out and towards a corner drugstore.

He was only in the store for a few seconds. He came out and strolled down the street. He noticed an open lot. He walked through a beaten-through path of the lot. And then he stopped...

"Aieeee!" That was his final shout.

The razor blade dropped from his hand in front of a rush of pouring blood. No, the Clarion could not be wrong!

STATEMENT OF THE OWNERSHIP, MANAGEMENT AND CIRCULATION REQUIRED BY THE ACT OF CONGRESS OF AUGUST 24, 1912, AS AMENDED BY THE ACTS OF MARCH 3, 1933, AND JULY 2, 1946, OF CHAMBER OF CHILLS MAGAZINE   published Monthly at   New York, N. Y.   for October 1, 1952.

1. The names and addresses of the publisher, editor, managing editor, and business managers are: Editor: Leon Harvey, 1860 Broadway, N. Y. C.; Managing Editor: Alfred Harvey, 1860 Broadway, N. Y. C.; Business Manager: Robert B. Harvey, 1860 Broadway, N. Y. C. Publisher: Witches Tales, Inc.   1860 Broadway, N. Y. C.

2. The owners are   Witches Tales, Inc.   1860 Broadway, N. Y. C.; Leon Harvey, 1860 Broadway, N Y. C.; Alfred Harvey, 1860 Broadway, N. Y. C.; Robert B. Harvey, 1860 Broadway, N. Y. C.

3. The known bondholders, mortgagees, and other security holders owning or holding 1 percent or more of total amount of bonds, mortgages, or other securities are: None.

4. Paragraphs 2 and 3 include, in cases where the stockholder or security holder appears upon the books of the company as trustee or in any other fiduciary relation, the name of the person or corporation for whom such trustee is acting; also the statements in the two paragraphs show the affiant's full knowledge and belief as to the circumstances and conditions under which stockholders and security holders who do not appear upon the books of the company as trustees, hold stock and securities in a capacity other than that of a bona fide owner.

(signed) ROBERT B. HARVEY, Business Manager
Sworn and subscribed to before me this 30th day of September, 1952.
Fred Stevens (My commission expires March 30th, 1954)

CHILLER DILLERS!

DO YOU KNOW THE *THE MAGIC FORMULA* WHICH WILL PERFORM THIS SEEMINGLY IMPOSSIBLE TRICK?

JUST PLACE A LARGE COIN IN THE CENTER OF AN OUTSPREAD HANDKERCHIEF AND THEN HOLDING THE DIAGONAL CORNERS OF THE HANDKERCHIEF, DRAW THEM TIGHTLY AND LIFT! THE COIN WILL BE TRAPPED IN THE CENTER OF THE CLOTH AND CAN BE EASILY MADE TO STAND ON EDGE!

YOU SET A FLAMING MATCH TO COMBUSTIBLE CIGARETTE PAPER YET *IT DOES NOT BURN!* DO YOU KNOW THIS INCREDIBLE TRICK?

PRESS THE CIGARETTE PAPER AGAINST THE SIDE OF A DRINKING GLASS, FOLLOWING THE CURVE OF THE GLASS! HOLDING THE PAPER SMOOTHLY BETWEEN THE THE THUMB AND FOREFINGER OF ONE HAND, APPLY THE LIGHTED MATCH TO THE PAPER WITH THE OTHER HAND! THE PAPER *WON'T BURN* BECAUSE THE GLASS ABSORBS THE HEAT AND PROTECTS IT FROM THE FLAME!

EL DIABLO

THE INITIATE INTO THE SUPERNATURAL CAN COMMAND SUGAR TO *FLOAT* ON A STEAMING CUP OF COFFEE! IT SINKS ONLY AT HIS WORD! DO YOU KNOW WHY?

BEFORE PERFORMING THE TRICK, SECRETLY DROP A LUMP OF SUGAR INTO THE COFFEE, SEEING THAT IT REMAINS STANDING ON ITS END, BELOW THE SURFACE OF THE LIQUID! THEN DROP LUMP NEATLY ON THE HIDDEN LUMP, SO THAT IT APPEARS TO BE *FLOATING!* AS THE HIDDEN LUMP MELTS, THE OTHER WILL SLOWLY SINK, SEEMINGLY AT THE COMMAND OF THE MAGICIAN!

A MAN SITS ALONE BEHIND THAT DOOR!..

I...I KNOW I *MUST* FIGHT! BUT I DON'T KNOW MY OPPONENT... I DON'T KNOW WHAT WILL HAPPEN IF I WIN...*OR LOSE!* AND I'M ALONE...*ALL ALONE!* I NEED HELP. I...

WAIT! SOMEONE AT THE DOOR. WHO--?

WHA---?

HELLO, VIRGIL. MY NAME'S SAM KANE. I LEARNED THAT YOU'RE FIGHTING... AND I'VE COME TO *HELP* YOU!

I SURE NEED IT, MR. KANE...BUT WHY ME? WHY SHOULD YOU HELP ME?

STOP WORRYING, AND DON'T ASK SILLY QUESTIONS. I THINK YOU'RE A *BORN FIGHTER!* YOU'RE *SURE* TO WIN!

YOU SEE...I'M A *MANAGER!* I KNOW ABOUT *FIGHTERS!* LISTEN TO ME...AND *YOU'LL WIN!* PUT THIS ON...AND LET'S GO!

OKAY, MR. KANE. ANY-THING YOU SAY. I'M READY.

SO THE FIGHTER AND HIS NEW MANAGER WALK BACK THROUGH THE CORRIDOR. THEY SEE BEFORE THEM THE SQUARED ARENA...BECKONING, LOOMING...

AHH! HERE IS THE OTHER FIGHTER....AND HIS MANAGER, TOO. COME...STEP INTO THE RING!

THE FIGHTER AND HIS MANAGER HEAR THE REFEREE'S VOICE...A VOICE THAT KNELLS... THAT TOLLS OMINOUSLY AS THEY CLIMB THROUGH THE ROPES...

YES, THAT'S IT. NOW...BOTH FIGHTERS WILL GO TO THE CENTER OF THE RING FOR ...UH... INSTRUCTIONS! HA HA!

THIS IS A FIGHT OF FATE! IF YOU LOSE...YOU WILL EXPERIENCE THE PANGS THAT ARE YOUR DESTINY! NOBODY KNOWS THEIR FATE...SO DO NOT LOSE! HA HA! REMEMBER... UNKNOWN FATE IS AT STAKE! NOW...GO TO YOUR CORNERS...

SO THE TWO CONTESTANTS GO TO THEIR CORNERS. IT'S SOON TO BEGIN...SECONDS TICK BY WITH THE SILENCE OF CRAWLING DEATH...THEN...

CLAANG!

GO TO HIM, VIRGIL. I KNOW I'M RIGHT! GO TO HIM!

THE TWO FIGHTERS TRADE BLOWS, AND THEN FALL INTO A CLINCH...

GO T...UGH! A CLINCH. THE FIGHT...WHY ARE WE FIGHTING?

I WISH I KNEW, BUSTER. BUT....ONE OF US GOT TO WIN!

3

...AND IT'S GOING TO BE *ME!*

UGH!

CLANG!

THE BELL...SAVED BY THE BELL! SO VIRGIL, WITH THANKS, WORKED HIS WAY BACK TO HIS CORNER.

THE BELL SAVED YOU, VIRGIL! YOU LEFT YOURSELF WIDE OPEN!

I...KNOW. SOMEONE...COMING OVER...HERE...

YOU ALMOST LOST IT THAT ROUND. *HA HA!* YOU SHOULD BE MORE CAREFUL ABOUT YOUR....*FATE!* I LEAVE YOU WITH THAT TO PONDER OVER.

I....I UNDERSTAND...

ROUND TWO! THERE'S THE BELL. NOW...CROSS HIM WITH YOUR LEFT...KEEP ON CROSSING HIM. THEN...*HIT HIM WITH THE RIGHT!* JUST...DO WHAT I SAY!

YEAH...YEAH...

CLANG!

VIRGIL REMEMBERS HIS MANAGER'S INSTRUCTIONS...

GOT TO CROSS HIM WITH...

...A LEFT...

4

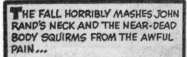

THE FALL HORRIBLY MASHES JOHN RAND'S NECK AND THE NEAR-DEAD BODY SQUIRMS FROM THE AWFUL PAIN...

...DYING...CAN'T BREATHE... THEY SHALL PAY...FOR... MY DEATH...

AGGRRAA...

AND LATER THAT NIGHT...

HA-HA! IT'S TOO BAD RAND COULDN'T BE WITH US TO SHARE THE PROFITS, ISN'T IT?

YES... TOO BAD INDEED!

THINGS WENT WELL FOR THE THREE MEN...AT LEAST FOR A YEAR. BUT THEN ONCE AGAIN ON THE ANNIVERSARY OF THE OPENING OF THE BRIDGE...

AIIEEK! IT'S HORRIBLE!

REVENGE!

AIIEEE!

IT'S GHASTLY!

2

THE VISION HAS A PURPOSE...AND THE VISION FINDS ITS GOAL!

IT'S--- WHAAAA!!

REMEMBER ME, ODEM?

YOU'RE DEAD KEEP AWAY!

BUT THE VISION DOESN'T KEEP BACK... IT HAS A TASK TO PERFORM!

WE KILLED YOU! YOU'RE---! AIIEEE!

AGGRRAAA!

CAREFUL, ODEM! YOU'RE TOO CLOSE TO THE LONDON BRIDGE!

REVENGE! GOODBYE ODEM. REVENGE!

FOR ANOTHER YEAR, THE GRAVE IS SILENT. BUT ONCE AGAIN ON THE ANNIVERSARY OF THE LONDON BRIDGE, A ROTTED CREATURE TAKES TO THE NIGHT...

REVENGE UPON THEM!

3

HE HAD TO TRY ONE LAST THING...

HA-HA! HERE I AM, RAND! COME AND GET ME!

I INTEND TO, MURDOCK!

RIGHT NOW!

I....WHAAA!

AGGRRRAAA!

AND THE FANTASTIC ASSOCIATION BETWEEN JOHN RAND AND THE LONDON BRIDGE CONTINUES!

YES, IT IS ONCE MORE A YEAR TO THE DAY LATER... AND A LONE AIRPLANE IS LOST IN THE ENCOMPASSING LONDON FOG! ITS LONE OCCUPANT IS *ENOS MORLEY!*

DRAT THIS FOG! IT'S THICK ENOUGH TO CUT!

5

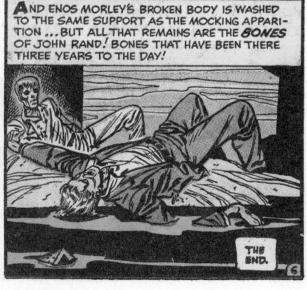

JEALOUSY

He watched them from the corner of his eye. He watched them move closer to each other, hold each other...

"At one time," he thought to himself, "she was mine. At one time, she looked at me like that. At one time, we sat together like that."

"Why did I have to be such a fool?" he tormented himself once more. "She loved me...she told me that time and time again! But I had to go away...I had to seek something more. And this is what I come to!"

No, it was no use. Her face, her look of childhood innocence haunted his mind and wouldn't let go.

"There must be something I can do! There must be a way that I can win her back!"

His eyes now pierced the darkness; he saw them again, and he knew that there was no way to win her back!

"Except...except..." The idea was being shaped in the twisted mind. His head was filled with the warped...the horrible...the inevitable thought of MURDER!

He waited patiently now. Soon she'd be taken home. Then her lover would pass through the park once more to go to his home. Then he'd have his chance. And no one would ever know...he'd plan it that way.

The minutes fled, and now it was late. He was taking her home. They passed him and she gave him a wee smile of acknowledgement. He nodded but didn't say a word.

He waited again as his pulse beat a roll of excitement. "You can't be afraid!" he said to himself. "Before you know it, it'll be over. And you'll have her!"

There were sounds now... slight thuds on the pavement. The lover was returning!

He stood beneath a tree and waited. Now the lover was coming near. He walked out from beneath the tree and stood in the lover's path.

The lover stopped and looked at him. He looked back. A fiery trail of hate burned between them.

"What do you want?" the lover finally said.

"Do I have to tell you?" was the reply.

"Why don't you leave us alone!" said the lover.

"It's not my make-up," was the reply.

And suddenly he sprang at the lover, letting loose all the venom that had twisted his insides! He clutched at his throat...he twisted...he forced him to the floor.

"No!" was all the lover could gasp.

And in a moment there was silence. The lover lay dead in a ghastly pool of blood. The hulking form of the victor stood over him and shouted his triumphant yell...

"Wooooffff! Wooofff!" And he wagged his tail behind him as he marched away.

STATEMENT OF THE OWNERSHIP, MANAGEMENT AND CIRCULATION REQUIRED BY THE ACT OF CONGRESS OF AUGUST 24, 1912, AS AMENDED BY THE ACTS OF MARCH 3, 1933, AND JULY 2, 1946, OF CHAMBER OF CHILLS MAGAZINE published Monthly at New York, N. Y.; for October 1, 1952.

1. The names and addresses of the publisher, editor, managing editor, and business managers are: Editor: Leon Harvey, 1860 Broadway, N. Y. C.; Managing Editor: Alfred Harvey, 1860 Broadway, N. Y. C.; Business Manager: Robert B. Harvey, 1860 Broadway, N. Y. C. Publisher: Witches Tales, Inc. 1860 Broadway, N. Y. C.

2. The owners are: Witches Tales, Inc. , 1860 Broadway, N. Y. C.; Leon Harvey, 1860 Broadway, N. Y. C.; Alfred Harvey, 1860 Broadway, N. Y. C.; Robert B. Harvey, 1860 Broadway, N. Y. C.

3. The known bondholders, mortgagees, and other security holders owning or holding 1 percent or more of total amount of bonds, mortgages, or other securities are: None.

4. Paragraphs 2 and 3 include, in cases where the stockholder or security holder appears upon the books of the company as trustee or in any other fiduciary relation, the name of the person or corporation for whom such trustee is acting; also the statements in the two paragraphs show the affiant's full knowledge and belief as to the circumstances and conditions under which stockholders and security holders who do not appear upon the books of the company as trustees, hold stock and securities in a capacity other than that of a bona fide owner.

(signed) ROBERT B. HARVEY, Business Manager
Sworn and subscribed to before me this 30th day of September, 1952.
Fred Stevens (My commission expires March 30th, 1954)

THADDEUS STEVENS THOUGHT HIS COLLECTION WAS COMPLETE. BUT THEN HE FOUND THE STRANGEST TROPHY OF THEM ALL. BUT *HE* COULDN'T APPRECIATE IT!

The COLLECTOR

THIS WAS A TYPICAL AFTERNOON AT THE HOME OF INTERNATIONALLY KNOWN HUNTER THADDEUS STEVENS...

HMMM....A PYGMY RHINO...WHITE ELEPHANT...WHY THIS IS THE MOST FABULOUS COLLECTION OF RARE ANIMALS I'VE EVER SEEN!

MORE EXTENSIVE THAN YOU'LL FIND IN *ANY* MUSEUM!

I SHOT, STUFFED, AND MOUNTED THEM ALL MYSELF. BUT LIFE'S PRETTY BORING NOW THAT THERE ARE NO *NEW* SPECIMENS I CAN ADD!

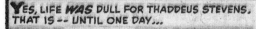

YES, LIFE *WAS* DULL FOR THADDEUS STEVENS. THAT IS -- UNTIL ONE DAY...

HMMM...RUMORS OF STRANGE, NEW ANIMAL SPECIMENS IN THE UNEXPLORED AREAS OF THE UPPER UBANGI COUNTRY. PROBABLY PURE IMAGINATION, BUT IF THERE'S ANYTHING I HAVEN'T BAGGED YET, I WANT A SHOT AT IT!

NOW HERE WAS A CHANCE FOR THADDEUS STEVENS. SO HE PACKED ALL HE NEEDED AND SET OUT FOR THE JUNGLE...

NO SIGN OF RARE ANIMALS SO FAR. MIGHT AS WELL PUSH ON AHEAD SO LONG AS I'M HERE!

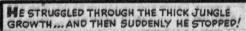

HE STRUGGLED THROUGH THE THICK JUNGLE GROWTH... AND THEN SUDDENLY HE STOPPED!

THAT STRANGE POOL...IT...IT SEEMS *ALIVE!* THE LIQUID TURNING AND WRITHING ON ITSELF. WHAT... WHAT CAN IT MEAN?

THADDEUS STEVENS WATCHED, CAUTIOUSLY, CAREFULLY... THEN A BIRD FELL INTO THE POOL, AND AS IT FLEW OUT...

WHY...IT...IT'S ANOTHER BIRD! ALIKE... AND YET SO HORRIBLY *UNLIKE* THE ONE THAT FELL IN!

THAT POOL MUST CONTAIN THE *ESSENCE OF LIFE*...THE STUFF FROM WHICH LIFE FIRST ROSE MILLIONS OF YEARS AGO! IT...IT'S PROBABLY THE LAST SUCH POOL IN EXISTENCE ANYWHERE ON EARTH!

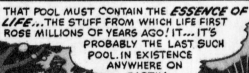

IT...IT CREATES LIFE...STRANGE GROTESQUE IMAGES OF WHATEVER COMES INTO CONTACT WITH IT! I CAN...WHY...WHAT AN IDEA! IT... IT'S *STUPENDOUS!*

2

BUT THADDEUS STEVENS' APPETITE WAS LARGE... VERY LARGE. HE JUST *HAD* TO ADD TO HIS COLLECTION!

C'MON, LITTLE FRIEND. IT'S TIME TO TAKE YOUR BATH!

OWW! LET GO, YOU LITTLE DEVIL!

YES, THE CUB LET GO...

AAAGGHHH!

AND IT WAS *THADDEUS STEVENS* WHO GOT THE BATH!

STRANGE SENSATION...LIKE SLIME CRAWLING ALL OVER MY SKIN...MUST GET OUT...*FAST!*

HE STAGGERED TO THE EDGE OF THE POOL. HE FELT SHARP TERROR STAB HIS HEART...AND HE LOOKED BEHIND HIM!

THE POOL...IT...IT'S FORMING AN IMAGE OF *ME*...A *HORRIBLE* IMAGE!

HE RAN...HE RAN WITH ALL HIS STRENGTH!

IT...IT'S COMING AFTER ME! IT...IT WANTS TO *CATCH ME!*

HE RAN WITH ALL HIS SOUL!

IT...IT'S LIKE ME... HORRIBLY LIKE ME!

4

New Styles Demand Smooth Flat Tummy

Amazing New French Undergarment Girdle
Makes You Look Your Best in New Fashions

MOST FLATTERING TUMMY CONTROL EVER CREATED

Wear TUMMY-TRIM **with** or **without** a girdle. TUMMY-TRIM is an entirely new kind of lightweight girdle. Its extra FLATTENING pressure is due to the criss-cross design plus a new strength elastic that s-t-r-e-t-c-h-e-s and adjusts automatically to shape your figure. Solid comfort! Better, more healthful posture! Exquisitely made! TUMMY-TRIM will actually improve your figure instantly and continue to better it day by day. The lacy trim completes its all-feminine picture. The four extra-length detachable adjustable garters are scientifically placed for comfort and to glamourize your legs.

Old fashioned girdles spoil your figure instead of improving it. Note how the "bulge" pokes out instead of being flat and graceful. No excuse now because TUMMY-TRIM holds you in.

Here's the modern, up-to-the-minute sylph-trim figure that TUMMY-TRIM will give you. A dramatic change to an eye-full dreamy figure of charm, grace, and desire.

10 DAYS FREE TRIAL

Order today. Send the coupon. Try on and wear your TUMMY-TRIM for 10 days . . . Test it! Examine it! If not 100% delighted with your new figure and the tremendous value, return for prompt refund of the full purchase price. Waist sizes 24 to 30, $2.98. Waist sizes 32 to 48, $3.98.

CUSTOM MADE FEATURES

• Automatically adjusts for perfect fit • Off or on in a jiffy • Lightweight . . . boneless • Extra strength, extra stretch, all-elastic Wonder-Web • Reinforced for long wear • Four 10-inch adjustable garters • Guaranteed to combine style and quality or no cost • Extra flattering—flattening • Girdle that walks with you . . . never will ride up.

FREE TRIAL COUPON

The S. J. Wegman Company, Dept. 117
836 Broadway, New York 3, N. Y.

RUSH my new TUMMY-TRIM three-in-one at once. If I am not thrillingly satisfied, I may return it after 10-day FREE trial for prompt refund of full purchase price.
Size .... (Waist size in inches)

☐ Send C.O.D. I will pay postman, on delivery, cost of the garment plus few cents postage.

☐ I enclose payment. The S. J. Wegman Company will pay postage. Same money-back guarantee.

Name ....

Address ....

CHAMBER OF CHILLS MAGAZINE, JULY, 1953, Vol. 1, No. 18, IS PUBLISHED BI-MONTHLY by WITCHES TALES, INC., 1860 Broadway, New York 23, N.Y. Entered as second class matter at the Post Office at New York, N.Y. under the Act of March 3, 1879. Single copies 10c. Subscription rates, 10 issues for $1.00 in the U.S. and possessions, elsewhere $1.50. All names in this periodical are entirely fictitious and no identification with actual persons is intended. Contents copyrighted, 1953, by Witches Tales, Inc., New York City. Printed in the U.S.A.

CHAMBER OF CHILLS Contents NO. 18

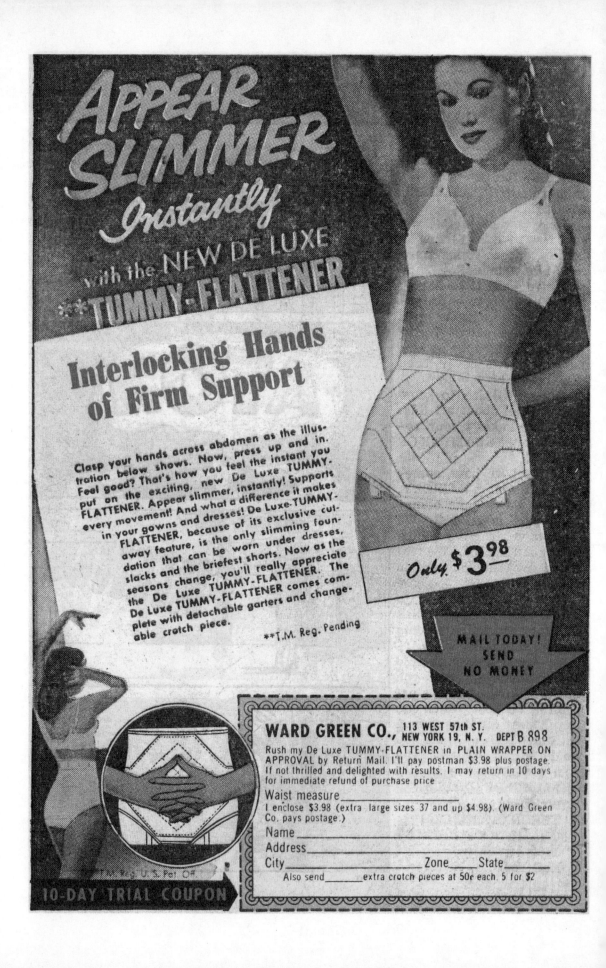

YOU CAN CERTAINLY *TALK*, MR. VESSELS!

THE BEST PART IS YET TO COME!

AFTER A FEW MONTHS, I TOOK OVER THE ADMINISTRATIVE REINS OF MARTHA'S LUMBER CONCERN. I WAS GOING TO BUILD IT INTO SOMETHING...AND *NOBODY*...NOT EVEN MARTHA...WAS GOING TO *STAND IN MY WAY!*...

LET'S GO FOR A WALK, AMOS! IT'S SO STUFFY IN HERE!

THERE'S NO *TIME* FOR WALKS! CAN'T YOU SEE THAT I'M *WORKING?*

FROM NOW ON...I'LL MAKE THE SUGGESTIONS. *UNDERSTAND?* YOU REMAIN IN THE BACKGROUND. I CAN'T HAVE YOU IN MY WAY. *UNDERSTAND?*

OF COURSE, AMOS!

"SHE UNDERSTOOD, ALL RIGHT! SHE *HAD* TO! SOON...I BEGAN TO BE CALLED AWAY...AND NOT TOO INFREQUENTLY."

WHERE ARE YOU GOING, AMOS?

TO THE CLUB. WE'RE HAVING A PARTY -- AND IT'S IMPORTANT THAT I ATTEND. INCIDENTALLY, IT'S A *MEN'S* PARTY-- SO YOU WON'T BE ABLE TO COME! GOODBYE!

BUT...I'M ALL ALONE!

SLAM!

WHAT HAPPENED AFTER THAT, MR. VESSELS?

THIS IS THE STORY OF MY LIFE, NICK. I WANT YOU TO *LEARN* FROM IT!

3

YEARS PASSED! THE LUMBER CONCERN WAS NOW A THRIVING BUSINESS! *I* HAD MADE IT SO! AND MARTHA...WELL, SHE WAS COMPLETELY SUBSERVIENT TO MY EVERY WISH! BUT...I WAS DISTURBED BY SOMETHING!

ANY MAIL FOR ME, AMOS?

WHY...UH ...NO! *WHO* WOULD *WRITE* TO YOU?

I'M GOING TO SEE JENKINS AT THE BANK. DON'T FORGET TO TAKE ANY MESSAGES FOR ME.

"ONCE I GOT OUTSIDE THE HOUSE, I TORE UP A LETTER INTO LITTLE PIECES. IT WAS A LETTER FOR MARTHA....*FROM HER BROTHER!* SHE HAD *OTHERS* BEFORE THIS...BUT LUCKILY I GOT TO THEM *BEFORE* HER. I RIPPED THEM ALL!"

HE CAN'T TAKE AWAY WHAT *I* BUILT UP. HE'LL ONLY STAND IN MY WAY! NOW... FOR JENKINS!

"AT THE BANK..."

EVERYTHING IS IN ORDER, MR. VESSELS... IN *PERFECT ORDER!*

THANK YOU, JENKINS! THANK YOU FOR KEEPING MY LITTLE *SECRET!*

I HAD FINALLY PERPETRATED MY ONE LAST PIECE OF BUSINESS. *NOTHING* COULD KEEP ME IN THAT LITTLE TOWN ANY LONGER. I CLEARED EVERYTHING FROM MY PATH.... AND WAS PACKING TO LEAVE...

"THEN... MARTHA ENTERED..."

AMOS! I.... UH... WHY, YOU'RE PACKING. WHERE ARE YOU GOING?

MARTHA! YOU SURPRISED ME!

WEATHER FORECAST

Tom Doby was a good weather forecaster. In fact, he was probably the best the Daily Call had ever employed. He knew all the latest scientific methods, and what's more he used them.

The Daily Call was very happy with Tom Doby. But Tom Doby wasn't very happy with himself!

Take the day he said to the managing editor, Steve Flowers: "Steve, you know it disappoints me to be wrong on any of my predictions. I'd like to say that it's going to be sunny, and know for sure that it is. Have everyone in this city know it's going to be sunny!"

Steve Flowers laughed, and then he said, "You're OK, Tom! And there's no need to worry yourself. We're perfectly satisfied with your work; I don't remember when we've had a better weatherman than you! So forget your mistakes, there aren't many of them anyhow!"

Tom Doby didn't say much after that. He knew that Steve Flowers couldn't understand what it would mean to be a perfectionist. He would only be wasting his breath.

But that night, Tom Doby went back to his thoughts. In fact he fell asleep still hoping for a fool-proof method of prediction.

Perhaps that was the reason it happened. Perhaps that was the reason, Tom Doby had the dream about a rainstorm!

The next morning the dream remained vividly in his mind. It was a crazy chance, but he'd take it. When he got to his office and checked on all his apparatus, the signs all pointed toward a sunny day. But Tom Doby said it would rain! And it did rain!

That's the way it started. That's the way it continued. Whatever Tom Doby dreamed, that's what would happen.

Tom explained his new method of prediction to his boss, Steve Flowers. Steve thought he was pulling his leg for awhile. But after three months of being 100 percent correct, after three months of defying scientific methods, Steve Flowers just had to believe him.

But then that awful night. Tom Doby went to bed at the same time he usually did. He slept in his usual position. But that night, Tom Doby had no dream!

When he awoke he didn't know what to think. Then he became frightened. Then he grew panicky. And then he rushed down to the office.

"What's up?" Steve Flowers questioned as Tom tore into his office.

"There'll be NO WEATHER today," shouted Tom.

"What are you talking about?" came back Steve.

"Have I ever been wrong?"

"No, but . . ."

"There are no but's," said Tom. "Put it in the paper!"

Yes, that day the paper did say that there would be no weather, though they did try to bury the report. But they shouldn't have. Tom Doby was correct as usual.

You see, that was the day the world came to an end!

MONSTERS OF HISTORY

THE *POLYPHEMUS*, THE ONE-EYED GIANT, THRIVED ON *HUMAN FLESH!* THE FAMOUS LEGENDARY HERO ULYSSES ESCAPED FROM HIS CLUTCHES BY PUTTING OUT HIS EYE WITH A HUGE STONE -- AND THEN FLEEING TO HIS SHIP -- AND SAFETY!...

MEDUSA, QUEEN OF MONSTERS HAD HAIR OF *HISSING SNAKES* THAT WAS SO HORRIBLE, IT TURNED MEN TO *STONE!* SHE WAS KILLED BY PERSEUS WHO, WHILE OBSERVING HER IMAGE IN A MIRROR, CUT OFF HER HEAD WITH A SWORD!

CHIMAERA WAS SHAPED LIKE A LION IN FRONT, A DRAGON IN BACK, AND A GOAT IN THE MIDDLE! IT WANDERED THE LAND, DESTROYING EVERYTHING IN ITS PATH -- UNTIL SLAIN BY THE HERO BELLEROPHON!

THE FURIES, THREE HIDEOUS WINGED FEMALES, PURSUED AND PUNISHED THE GUILTY! NO CREATURES WERE SO DREADED AS THESE--WHO RELENTLESSLY HOUNDED THEIR VICTIMS TO DOOM!

THE HYDRA WAS A MONSTER OF MANY HEADS! FOR EACH HEAD THAT WAS CUT OFF, *TWO* WOULD GROW IN ITS PLACE, MAKING IT ALMOST IMPOSSIBLE TO DESTROY HIM! HERCULES, HOWEVER, SUCCEEDED IN SLAYING HIM BY BURNING EIGHT OF THE HEADS-- AND BURYING THE NINTH UNDER A ROCK!

HECATE, GODDESS OF SORCERY AND WITCHCRAFT HAD A KINGDOM THAT EXTENDED OVER THE ENTIRE UNIVERSE! IT WAS THOUGHT SHE HAUNTED CROSS-ROADS ON THE BLACKEST OF NIGHTS--WAITING TO LURE NEW VICTIMS TO HER EVIL CULT!

BRACE YOUR-SELF FOR THE SHOCK OF YOUR LIFE IN...

ATOM

AT THE EDGE OF A SECRET TESTING GROUND FOR NEW WEAPONS, TWO SCIENTISTS TALK. ONE OF THEM IS *YOU!* YOUR NAME IS *TERRY BRADLEY!*

NOW, TERRY, THE FINAL ADJUSTMENTS ARE UP TO YOU! BUT REMEMBER, WE SET THE BOMB OFF AT *TWO SHARP!* YOU MUST BE CLEAR OF THE *DANGER AREA* BY THEN!

DON'T WORRY, DAVIS, THAT WILL GIVE ME *PLENTY OF TIME* FOR THE FEW THINGS I HAVE TO DO!

YOU START TO DO THOSE FEW THINGS, BUT...

NOW JUST TO CONNECT THESE LAST FEW WIRES, AND I CAN CLEAR OUT OF... *AHHHH!*

Z-Z-Z-ZZSHH!

YOU SHOULD HAVE KNOWN ABOUT *LOOSE WIRES* BY NOW. BUT AT THE LAST SECOND YOU'VE BECOME *CARELESS*...AND NOW THERE'S *NOTHING* YOU CAN DO AS THE CLOCK HANDS SWING AROUND!

TWO MINUTES TO GO! THE AREA IS *COMPLETELY CLEARED!* GET READY, GENTLEMEN, FOR THE BLAST!

IT'S ONLY A MINUTE TO GO NOW...AND AT LAST YOU RECOVER...

ONLY A *MINUTE!* I...I'VE GOT TO GET OUT OF HERE! GOT TO *STOP* THEM! I'M *TOO CLOSE!* WAIT! *WAIT!!*

BUT THEY *DON'T* HEAR YOU...

WAIT! WA.... AAAIIEEE!!

CAAARRR

OOMMMM

YOUR VOICE IS LOST IN THE SPLITTING EXPLOSION, AND ONCE AGAIN YOU'RE THROWN INTO A LONG, DEEP UNCONSCIOUSNESS, BUT LATE THAT NIGHT, YOU ARISE...

UHHHHAAAH! WH... WHERE AM I? OOHOO... PAIN... *PAIN!!*

THE EXPLOSION! NOW I REMEMBER...I WAS CAUGHT! WATER! MUST HAVE WATER!! I... I'M *BURNING UP* INSIDE!!

YOU'RE *LUCKY* YOU CAN'T SEE YOUR FACE!

2

ALL YOU KNOW IS THAT HORRIBLE BURNING DEEP INSIDE YOU. BUT AS YOU WALK DAZEDLY TOWARD THE BASE...

I...I FEEL SO HOT...BURNING ALL OVER! MUST GET SOME WATER! BURNING UP! MY HANDS...THEY...THEY GLOW IN THE DARK!

YOU RUSH TO DR. DAVIS' LAB...

MMMM—THIS NEW COMPOUND OUGHT TO INTENSIFY THE RATION OF... HUH!! WHAT IN THE WORLD... TERRY!!

TAP TAP TAP

WHAT HAPPENED TO YOU?! HERE...LET ME HELP Y...

NO! DON'T TOUCH ME!! I...I THINK I'M RADIO-ACTIVE...POISONED! WATER...PLEASE, WATER! THERE'S A FIRE IN ME!

HELP ME! (GULP-GULP!) GETTING WORSE ALL THE TIME...DRIVING ME CRAZY! CAN'T STAND IT! (GULP-GULP!) HELP ME...

AMAZING! WHY, YOU GLOW LIKE A NEON TUBE! I MUST FIND A WAY TO KEEP YOU ALIVE! WHY THIS WILL ASTOUND THE SCIENTIFIC WORLD!

LOOK, THIS IS TERRY! I GOT CAUGHT IN THAT EXPLOSION FOR YOU! YOU'RE THE ONLY ONE WHO CAN SAVE ME! DON'T LOOK AT ME AS I WERE IN A TEST TUBE! I'M A HUMAN BEING!

KEEP BACK, YOU FOOL! DO YOU WANT TO DESTROY ME TOO? NO- YOU'RE NOT HUMAN NOW! YOU'RE A CREATURE FROM ANOTHER WORLD ...YOU'RE THE NEW ATOMIC MAN!!

YOU CAN'T CONTROL YOUR EMOTIONS ANY LONGER...

YOU FIEND! I'M DYING, AND YOU BLABBER! I'M BEING TORTURED BY INTERNAL FIRE AND YOU...YOU...

STAY BACK!...YOU'RE MAD..MA... AHHAH ARGHGH!!

3

THEY FOUND DAVIS A SHORT WHILE LATER...

LOOK! SOMETHING *TERRIBLE* HAS HAPPENED TO HIM!

HIS THROAT! YOU CAN SEE WHERE HE'S BEEN *CHOKED!* IT *GLOWS!* QUICK- WE'D BETTER GET SECURITY OVER HERE IN A HURRY!

BUT YOU'RE SOMEWHERE ELSE...FIGHTING THE HORROR THAT SEARS YOUR INSIDES...FIGHTING YOUR MIND THAT SHOUTS ONLY HATE!

HARRY, DO *YOU* SEE WHAT *I* SEE?! WHAT IS IT...AN ADVERTISING STUNT!? HARRY- HE...IT'S COMING TOWARD US!

EASY, NOW...I'M SURE IT ISN'T ANYTHING TO BE FRIGHTENED OF...

THEY *ALL* HATE ME!

AHHHHH!!

SMACK!

EEEEEEE!!

THEN YOU RUN...

HE'S DEAD... DEAD...

HALT! OR I'LL SHOOT!

YOU FLEE TO THE SUBURBS. YOU LOOK EVERYWHERE, ANYWHERE FOR A PLACE TO HIDE. AND YOUR THROAT ROARS FOR WATER!

BACK! BACK, YOU BRUTE...I MUST HAVE WATER...

NEIGHHHHH!!

AHHHHH...

4

FINALLY, YOU FIND A HIDING PLACE...

THEY'LL NEVER FIND ME IN HERE! NO ONE WOULD THINK OF LOOKING FOR A *LIVE* MAN IN A GRAVEYARD!

HEY, JOE! IS THAT...A ...A KIND OF *GLOW* COMING FROM THAT WINDOW?

HOLY SMOKES! C'MON, LET'S GET OUT OF HERE!

BUT THE NEXT DAY YOU ARISE AND YOUR THROAT IS SCREAMING. YOU RUN FROM YOUR SANCTUARY... YOU DASH THROUGH THE FIELDS... AND YOU SEE A *HOUSE!*

I MUST SOOTHE MY THROAT... I MUST SOOTHE MY THROAT!

YOU USE EVERY BIT OF STRENGTH IN YOUR BODY...YOU PUSH...

OPEN... *OPEN!*

AND FINALLY IT OPENS!

THANK GOD, NO ONE IS HOME! THERE...OVER THERE... PERHAPS *THAT* CAN HELP ME!

NO! DON'T BE A FOOL!

THIS SHOULD DO IT... IT'S GOT TO DO IT...

DON'T LOSE YOUR HEAD AGAIN! REMEMBER, REMEMBER THAT WHISKEY IS 48% ALCOHOL...

AND IT BURNS!

AIEEEE!

96 PROOF

THE END

5

1000
LIVE BABY TURTLES
GIVEN AWAY
WITH THIS OFFER

EVERY BOY AND GIRL LOVES THESE CLEAN LITTLE PETS. DELIVERED HEALTHY AND SAFE IN A SPECIAL MOSS-PROTECTED PACKAGE.

Here's one of the most exciting toys you've ever owned. Just think — a baby turtle all your own. What's more, a real growing garden to keep him in, a garden you plant and grow all by yourself. You can teach him to recognize you when you feed him. Watch him swim — see how he pulls his head and feet into his shell when he's frightened. You can have turtle races — you can make a little house for him to live in — and all the time you can watch how the lovely, soft grass grows — see and smell the beautiful flowers. You'll amaze your friends with how much you know about animals and plants.

MAGIC ROCK GARDEN
Grows Real Grass & Flowers in 4 Days

only $1.69

HERE'S OUR OFFER

You pay only $1.69 for the rock garden and turtle . . . AND you must be 100% delighted or money back. Only 3 orders to a customer with this special offer. Hurry Coupon!

FEATURES
Everything You Need

You get all these items — you don't need anything else. Plenty of Magic grass seeds . . . Magic soil, lovely flower seeds . . . Practical attractive container . . . Bright-colored metal butterfly . . . American Flag . . . Parasol that opens and closes . . . Simulated rocks. Plant food. Many other exciting features.

Magic Seeds in Magic Soil

A real growing Rock Garden — about 100 square inches of sweet grass and bright lovely flowers — for you to care for. When the flowers grow you can pluck a bouquet for your mother or friend. When the grass grows too high you will have to cut and trim it. And all the time you will have a beautiful garden you can be proud of and show off to your friends. You'll learn many useful things, too — it will even help you understand many things they teach at school.

FRIEND!

DID YOU EVER *COUNT ON* ANYBODY? *I DID!* DID YOU EVER HAVE A *PAL* WHO WOULD DO *ANYTHING* FOR YOU? *I DID!* YES, GEORGE FIT ALL THESE THINGS... FOR HE WAS MY PAL ...MY BUDDY...MY...

I WAS HAVING MY TROUBLES WITH LOUISE. I WAS SURE THERE WAS SOMEONE ELSE...

BUT... LOUISE?

SEE YOU *TONIGHT,* ALBERT!

1908

BUS STOP

SOMETHING'S GOT TO BE DONE. BUT... *WHAT?*

THAT'S IT!! I'LL ASK... GEORGE!

SNAP!

BUY NOW!

1

HI, AL! HEY... *CHEER UP!* NOTHING CAN BE *THAT* BAD!

I NEED YOUR HELP, GEORGE. IT'S ABOUT *LOUISE!*

I--I KNOW SOMEONE ELSE IS SEEING HER. IF I DON'T DO *SOMETHING...I'LL LOSE HER!* BUT... I'M STYMIED! WHAT CAN I DO, GEORGE?

THAT'S A CINCH! *BE A MAN! SHOW* HER WHAT A *MAN* CAN *DO!* YOU'RE SEEING HER TONIGHT, AREN'T YOU?

SO?

OKAY! NOW... TONIGHT...

I KNEW I COULD RELY ON GEORGE. AFTER ALL...HE WAS MY *FRIEND!* SO...THAT NIGHT...AFTER I PICKED UP LOUISE...

HURRY, ALBERT! WE DON'T WANT TO MISS ANY...

SUDDENLY, LOUISE SHRIEKED... HER SENTENCE CUT IN TWO...

YAAH!

THERE WAS *A MAN DANGLING IN AN ALLEY!* I RUSHED IN...

I'LL SAVE HIM, LOUISE!

I CUT THE MAN DOWN! BUT...THIS MAN WASN'T DEAD! HE WASN'T EVEN *HALF DEAD!* IT WAS *GEORGE*...THE ROPE UNDER HIS ARMS... INSTEAD OF HIS CHIN! BUT...

ALBERT!

2

LOUISE WASN'T IMPRESSED!

ARE YOU FINISHED? WE'VE WASTED A LOT OF TIME! NOW...WE'LL BE *LATE* FOR THE *THEATRE!*

BUT... LOUISE...

COME ON, ALBERT!

GEORGE'S SCHEME HAD FAILED! BUT...THE NEXT DAY...AT THE OFFICE...

IT DIDN'T GO OVER, DID IT, GEORGE?

NOPE! SHE'S A HARD ONE TO PLEASE, ALL RIGHT! BUT... DON'T LET IT GET YOU DOWN, ALBERT!

THERE'S MORE THAN ONE WAY TO SKIN A CAT-OR A *WOMAN!* DON'T WORRY, ALBERT, I GOT A *LOT* OF TRICKS UP MY SLEEVE!

YOU'RE A PAL, GEORGE!

THINK NOTHING OF IT! NOW...THE NEXT TIME YOU HAVE A DATE WITH LOUISE...

YEAH, GEORGE, YEAH?

BOY, THAT GEORGE COULD THINK THEM UP! HE'D DO *ANYTHING* FOR ME! SO A FEW NIGHTS LATER...WHEN LOUISE AND I WERE WALKING...

YOU'VE BEEN EXTREMELY THOUGHTFUL TONIGHT, ALBERT!

YES! I....

3

THEN SUDDENLY...

STICK 'EM UP!

YAAH!

BUT...I WAS PREPARED FOR THIS...AND *HOW!* I LET LOOSE WITH A RIGHT TO THE GUNMAN'S MIDSECTION...

WHY, YOU....!!! *TAKE THAT!*

UGH!

AND I FOLLOWED THAT WITH A TERRIFIC RIGHT TO HIS FACE...ONLY THE GUNMAN WAS...*GEORGE!*

I KNOCKED GEORGE DOWN...I WAS SORRY FOR THAT! BUT...I WAS SORRIER BECAUSE LOUISE TOOK THE WRONG ATTITUDE!

YOU'RE A *BRUTE,* ALBERT HIGGINS... KNOCKING THAT *POOR MAN* DOWN LIKE THAT! GOODBYE!

THE NEXT MORNING...GEORGE CAME IN WITH A HUFF...A BLACK EYE AND A NEW SCHEME...

ALBERT, YOU'VE GO TO GO A LONG WAY TO *IMPRESS* LOUISE! YOU'VE GOT TO SHOW THAT YOU'RE WILLING TO *DIE* FOR HER! THAT'S WHAT THESE *PILLS* ARE FOR!

PILLS... DIE...?!!

SURE! PROVE THAT IT'S... *HER LOVE*...OR *DEATH!* THEN TAKE *ONE* OR *TWO OF THESE* ...DON'T WORRY, THEY'RE SUGAR-COATED! WHEN SHE SEES HOW *SINCERE* YOU ARE...TELL HER TO *DIAL* MY NUMBER!

I'LL COME AS THE *DOCTOR*...AND ...HEH! HEH!...*SAVE* YOU! AS *FRIEND* TO *FRIEND,* ALBERT ...THIS ONE *HAS* TO WORK!

POISON

4

YES, GEORGE HAD THE SCHEME! SO...A FEW MINUTES AGO...RIGHT IN FRONT OF LOUISE...I SHOVED TWO OF THOSE SUGAR-COATED GLOBES DOWN MY THROAT!

ALBERT...NO...*NO!* OH, IT'S TOO LATE! YOU'VE DONE IT! WHAT CAN I DO? *WHAT CAN I DO?*

YOU SEE HOW MUCH I LOVE YOU! BUT...YOU CAN SAVE ME BY CALLING *GEORGE TRUMBULL'S* NUMBER. HE'S MY...*DOCTOR!*

YES... RIGHT AWAY...

I'M LAUGHING TO MYSELF. IT'S A GOOD JOKE, BUT WHAT'S *THAT?* WHERE'D THIS *FOG* COME FROM? SOMEONE'S AT THE DOOR!

I-IT LOOKS LIKE *GEORGE!* MY...FRIEND...WITH LOUISE...*KISSING?* OH, THE FOG!

WHO'S THAT TALKING?...A BELL-LIKE VOICE... *GEORGE'S* VOICE...TALKING TO *ME!*

ALBERT, I'VE SOMETHING TO TELL YOU! YOU SEE...*I* WAS YOUR *RIVAL!* WE...LOUISE AND I...HAD TO GET RID OF YOU! YOU THOUGHT WE WERE PLAYING TRICKS! AND...WE *WERE!* BUT ...THE TRICKS WERE *ON YOU!*

THE FOG'S A HAZE...A *BLACK* HAZE...

THE PILLS YOU TOOK WERE POISON... *SUGAR-COATED POISON!* YOU'VE BEEN A GOOD SPORT, ALBERT...A REAL *FRIEND!*

THE END

I guess he's been right all the time. But I just didn't realize it till now.

I remember the first time he gave me that look. It had only been a week that I had been working for him.

"Mr. Robertson," I said. "Don't you think the blue tie would look better with the suit?"

He gave me that terrible look then, and screamed, "Philips! I pay you to be my butler! To do things at my bidding! Not to make suggestions!"

"Yes, sir," I answered. "I'll know better the next time."

But I didn't know better the next time. Mr. Robertson had done an awful lot of drinking that night. I saw that his wife had been more than just a little irritated. I pardoned myself and said:

"Mr. Robertson, I believe your wife is a bit angry at..."

He stopped me, and there was that look again.

"Philips, just get your dirty nose out of my affairs! If my wife is angry, SHE'LL tell me! Now get out of my sight!"

That's what happened then, and I'm ashamed to say I didn't learn. The next time was a corker.

Mr. Robertson's little daughter was to come home from boarding school. He hadn't seen her for three months, and she could only be home for a day. And Mr. Robertson had made a date to go to the theater. I thought he had forgotten about the girl, so I said:

"Mr. Robertson, I believe you've forgotten that your daughter will be home today."

"I haven't forgotten a thing," he answered, "but I believe YOU have! I told you I didn't want your stupid meddling! Remember it the next time!" Yes, he also gave me that look.

There was still another time. That was his anniversary, and his wife had planned a surprise party.

We were the only ones home, and he was about to leave for the evening. I thought I should at least hint at what was to be.

"Mr. Robertson," I said. "I believe today is your anniversary, and I think your wife might be..."

No, he didn't let me finish.

"Philips!" he said, and once more with that ugly look, "this is the last time I'll warn you! Keep out of my affairs!"

"Yes, sir," I answered, and this time I told myself I'd learn.

So now I have. And I won't get that awful look again. I saw his wife put the poison into his wine glass. I saw it minutes ago... long before he even drank it! But, you know, you live and learn.

So now I've learned not to be nosey. Heh, but it's a shame that he can't wholly appreciate it!

The HOUSE!

A NEW COUPLE HAS JUST BOUGHT THE HOUSE.

...AND I SERVED MISS ABIGAIL AND MISS HESTER *FAITHFULLY* FOR MANY YEARS IN THIS HOUSE... I HOPE TO SERVE *YOU* AS WELL!

MRS. MORGAN AND I REQUIRE VERY LITTLE, BATES. WE GO OUR *SEPARATE* WAYS MOST OF THE TIME!

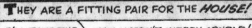

THEY ARE A FITTING PAIR FOR THE *HOUSE!*

I'LL TAKE THE ROOM IN THE NORTH WING, EMMA! AND THE *LESS* WE SEE OF EACH OTHER THE BETTER!

YOU NEEDN'T WORRY, ARNOLD! I TAKE NO PLEASURE IN SEEING YOUR FACE -- OR HEARING YOUR VOICE! GOODNIGHT!

AND THAT EVENING, THE HOUSE WATCHES A STRANGE SCENE...

MR. MORGAN! MR. MORGAN! WAKE UP! YOU MUST *LISTEN* TO ME!

WHAT ARE YOU BABBLING ABOUT AT THIS HOUR, BATES?

THEY HAVE COME TO ME AGAIN! MISS ABIGAIL AND MISS HESTER HAVE ORDERED ME TO *KILL* YOU BOTH... TO DESTROY THE STRANGERS ...IN THEIR *HOUSE*!

THE TWO OLD SPINSTERS WHO OWNED THE HOUSE BEFORE US? WHY THEY'VE BEEN *DEAD* FOR FIFTEEN YEARS!

I *KNOW*! I WATCHED THEM DIE IN THIS ROOM! BUT I *WARN* YOU, SIR, THEY'LL PLAGUE ME UNTIL I *MURDER* YOU IN YOUR BEDS!

GO TO BED, BATES, YOU SIMPLY HAVE TOO *VIVID* AN IMAGINATION! MISS ABIGAIL AND MISS HESTER ARE RESTING PEACEFULLY IN THE GRAVEYARD BEYOND THE HILL!

BATES LEFT THE ROOM...AND LEFT ARNOLD MORGAN ALONE WITH HIS THOUGHTS...

THE OLD FOOL REALLY THINKS THOSE TWO HAGS ARE ORDERING HIM TO KILL! YOU'D THINK I HAD ENOUGH TROUBLE JUST WITH *EMMA*! BUT...

THAT'S IT! IF I COULD PERSUADE HIM TO KILL *EMMA*--AND-- IT *CAN* BE DONE!

AND THE FOLLOWING NIGHT HE TRIED...

LISTEN TO ME, BATES -- I AM THE SPIRIT OF YOUR OLD MISTRESS! THE WOMAN IN THE HOUSE *MUST DIE!* SHE HAS INTRUDED INTO OUR DOMAIN!

WH~?

2

KILL KILL KILL KILL KILL KILL KILL KILL KILL

I HEAR! SHE WILL DIE THIS VERY NIGHT!

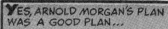

YES, ARNOLD MORGAN'S PLAN WAS A GOOD PLAN...

BATES! WHAT ARE YOU DOING HERE? PUT THAT DOWN...

YOU SHALL BE AT REST, MISS ABIGAIL! IN ONE MOMENT YOU SHALL KNOW PEACE AGAIN!

IT WAS A SUCCESSFUL PLAN, TOO!

ARNOLD MORGAN ENJOYED THE MORNING AFTER...

I--I COULD NOT HELP IT! THE VOICES...THE VOICES...HOW THEY TORMENTED ME---

DON'T WORRY YOURSELF, BATES... YOU'RE NOT RESPONSIBLE! AND THE WORLD IS BETTER OFF WITHOUT HER!

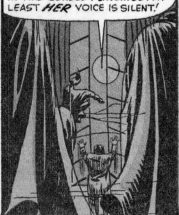

AND SO THE HOUSE WAS QUIET FOR AWHILE...BUT ONLY FOR AWHILE...

GADS, IT'S TOO QUIET IN THIS CURSED PLACE...BUT AT LEAST HER VOICE IS SILENT!

IT CAME TO LIFE VERY SOON!

YAAH-H! LISTEN TO US--LEAVE THIS HOUSE BEFORE YOU ARE KILLED BY BATES! WE WILL PERMIT NO STRANGERS HERE!

IT...IT WAS ONLY AN ILLUSION... A WAKING NIGHTMARE... I'VE BEEN ALONE TOO MUCH HERE ...GOT TO REST ...GOT TO GET SOME SLEEP!

3

BUT AS DAYS PASSED, ARNOLD MORGAN'S "NIGHTMARES" DIDN'T...

LEAVE THIS HOUSE! LEAVE THIS HOUSE ...OR BATES SHALL KILL YOU!

KILL YOU... KILL YOU...

STOP! STOP! I CAN'T GO ON THIS WAY! LEAVE ME ALONE!

AND NEXT MORNING HE TOOK A LONG LOOK AT BATES...

HE DOES LOOK MAD AND TORMENTED... AS IF HE IS WAITING TO KILL ME... BUT IF I COULD DESTROY THE SPIRITS...

THEY SAY THAT THE SPIRITS OF THE DEAD CAN BE DESTROYED... BY DESTROYING THEIR LIKENESSES! IF I SHOULD BURN THOSE PORTRAITS....!!

YES! I WILL BURN THEM! AND I'LL BE FREE OF SUDDEN DEATH! FREE OF THE SPIRITS OF DARKNESS!

NO! NO! YOU MUSTN'T! WE WISH TO WANDER THE EARTH FOREVER! YOU CAN'T...

IT'S WORKING! IT'S WORKING!

BURN AND DIE! THIS HOUSE IS MINE NOW-- MINE ALONE! NOBODY-- NOTHING-- CAN TAKE IT FROM ME!

4

BUT THE HOUSE WAS *NOT* TO BE SILENCED. ARNOLD MORGAN HADN'T FIGURED *EVERYTHING!*

KILL HIM, BATES! LET HIM FEEL THE COLD EDGE OF STEEL CUTTING INTO HIS *EVIL* HEART!

DIE!

HAVE I SERVED YOU WELL, MISTRESS?

YOU MAY SERVE ME FOREVER, BATES -- IN THIS HOUSE -- WHERE I *ALONE* SHALL REIGN AS MISTRESS!

BUT EMMA MORGAN HADN'T FIGURED CORRECTLY EITHER...

OH, NO! NO!

DID YOU THINK YOU COULD ESCAPE FROM YOUR *BELOVED* HUSBAND SO EASILY? YOU'VE ALWAYS BEEN A *FOOL,* EMMA!

WE SHALL REIGN *TOGETHER* IN THIS HOUSE! AND BATES SHALL BE OUR FAITHFUL SERVANT!

THEN EVEN IN DEATH WE ARE CHAINED TO EACH OTHER! *EVEN IN DEATH!*

MISS ABIGAIL -- MISS HESTER -- *REST IN PEACE!* MY MISSION IS DONE!

YES, THE HOUSE IS... A HOUSE WITH- OUT AN *EXIT!*

THE END

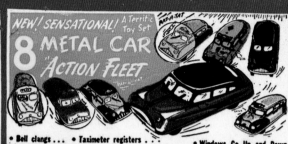

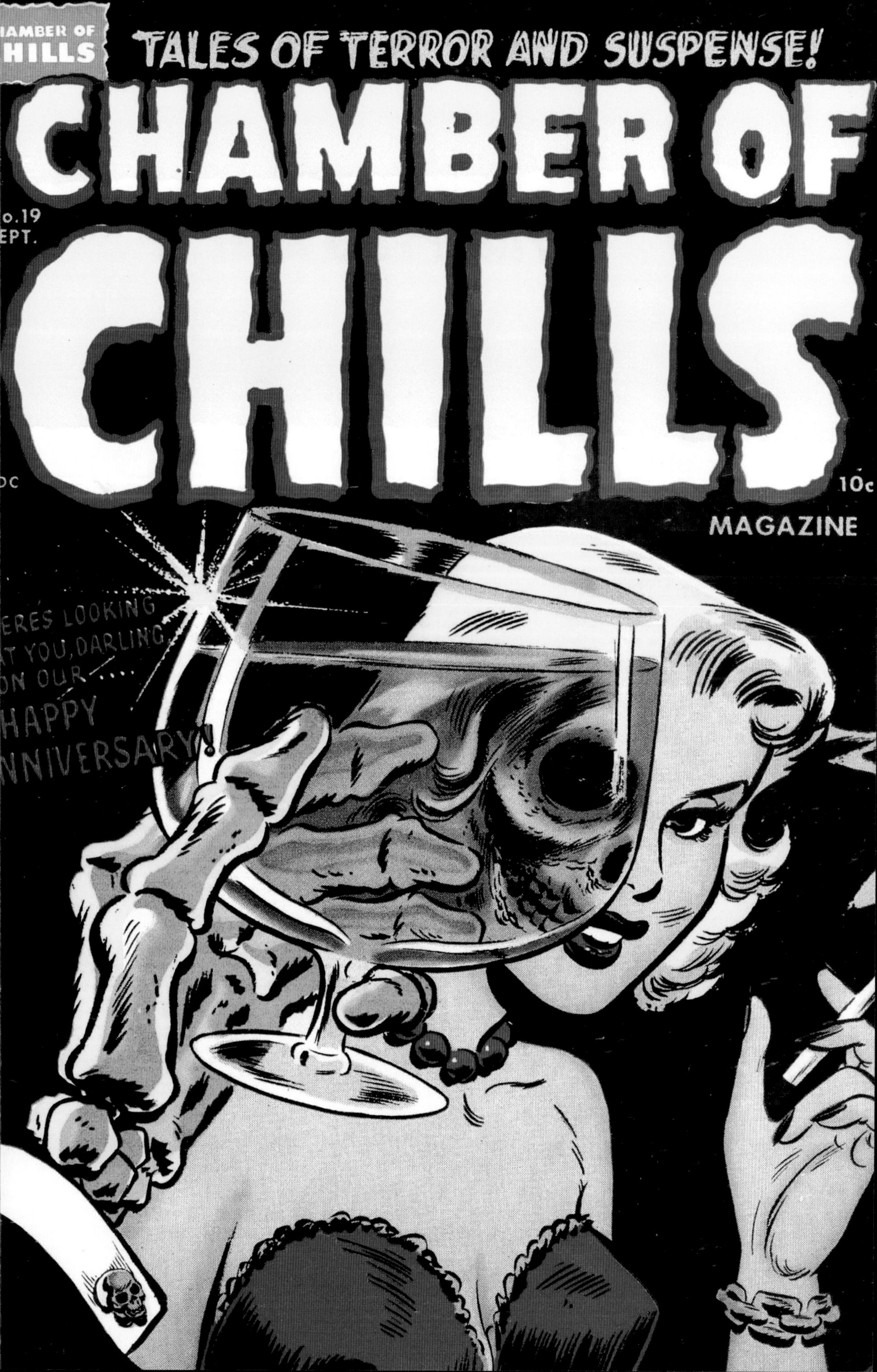
CHAMBER OF CHILLS
TALES OF TERROR AND SUSPENSE!
CHAMBER OF
CHILLS
No.19
SEPT.
10c
MAGAZINE
HERE'S LOOKING AT YOU, DARLING ON OUR ..... HAPPY ANNIVERSARY!

CHAMBER OF CHILLS MAGAZINE, SEPTEMBER, 1953, Vol. 1, No. 19, IS PUBLISHED BI-MONTHLY by WITCHES TALES, INC., 1860 Broadway, New York 23, N.Y. Entered as second class matter at the Post Office at New York, N.Y under the Act of March 3, 1879. Single copies 10c. Subscription rates, 10 issues for $1.00 in the U.S. and possessions. elsewhere $1.50. All names in this periodical are entirely fictitious and no identification with actual persons is intended. Contents copyrighted, 1953. by Witches Tales, Inc., New York City. Printed in the U.S.A.

CHAMBER OF CHILLS Contents NO. 19

AT LAST! A CHROME RESTORER THAT WORKS!

TURN THIS

INTO THIS

Amazing new 2-way chrome protector wipes away rust —pits—corrosion—in just 2 minutes! Stops rust from forming! Keeps chrome mirror-bright!

Now keep your bumpers, grillwork, window-frames, all chrome on your car sparkling bright as the day you bought it! Keep it rust-free for life! No matter how badly pitted or scarred, this sensational new 2-Way Chrome Protector wipes it Mirror-Bright, prevents new rust and corrosion from forming!

$2

ONE APPLICATION LASTS ENTIRE SEASON—gives you safe, fool-proof protection against vicious biting erosions of **SALT AIR—SUN—RAIN—SLEET**—etc. **101 USES**—for fishing reels, boat trims, bicycles, sporting equipment, etc. Household appliances, farm equipment, toys, any chromed object, etc.

Complete Chrome Protector Kit contains:

1—Bottle of **RUST REMOVER** chemical with special applicator. Enough to remove all rust from car.

2—Can of **PROTECTOR** chrome rust preventer and applicator. Enough for years of safe protection.

RESULTS ABSOLUTELY GUARANTEED OR MONEY BACK!

Enclose $2, check or money order with name and address. C.O.D. orders plus postal charges. Get Your Chrome Kit Now!

H. SEARS INDUSTRIES 15th Floor
1860 Broadway, New York 23, N. Y.

H. SEARS INDUSTRIES 15th Floor
1860 Broadway, New York 23, N. Y.

Please send me (   ) CHROME KITS at $2.00 each. It is understood that you guarantee excellent results or I may return package within 10 days for a refund of my purchase price.

Name_____

Address_____

City_____Zone____State_____

( ) Send C.O.D. I will pay postman on delivery plus postage and handling charges. (You save approximately 57c by enclosing $2.00 in cash, check or money order.)

THIS IS THE SEASON OF MERRIMENT, OF *MARRIAGE*, OF MIRTH. AND IN LINE WITH THE TIME OF THE YEAR, WE OF *CHAMBER OF CHILLS* HAVE OUR OWN SPECIAL WAY OF WISHING YOU A...

HAPPY ANNIVERSARY

THE LONG SUMMER DAY IS ENDING. THE SOFT CURTAIN OF TWILIGHT FALLS OVER THE CITY. AND IN A LITTLE HOUSE CHARLOTTE HUMS HAPPILY AS SHE GETS READY FOR THE GREAT EVENT...

BE PATIENT, DEAR. I'LL JOIN YOU AS SOON AS THE CHAMPAGNE IS CHILLED. THEN WE'LL START OUR *ANNIVERSARY PARTY* WITH THE USUAL TOAST TO ANOTHER YEAR OF *HAPPINESS!*

OUR *TENTH!* IT'S HARD TO REALIZE WE'VE BEEN TOGETHER IN THIS HOUSE FOR TEN LONG YEARS! HOW TIME FLIES WHEN ONE IS *HAPPY!*

①

I NEVER THOUGHT THE DAY WOULD COME WHEN YOU'D BE *THIS* FAITHFUL TO ME, FRED DARLING!

I REMEMBER THAT TIME YOU SAID YOU NEVER WANTED TO SEE ME AGAIN!

I MEAN IT! I DON'T KNOW HOW I STOOD YOU *THIS* LONG, YOU -- YOU *LEECH!*

FRED! YOU DON'T KNOW WHAT YOU'RE SAYING! YOU DON'T KNOW HOW MUCH I LOVE YOU!

IT MUST HAVE BEEN ONE OF YOUR MOODS...BECAUSE IT WAS SO EASY TO CONVINCE YOU THAT YOU'D BE BETTER OFF WITH ME THAN WITH THAT FLIGHTY BETTY MERRIWEATHER!

YOU KNOW, DEAR... PHYSICAL BEAUTY WEARS OFF WITH YEARS, BUT *I* CAN OFFER YOU SOMETHING *LASTING!*

I GET WHAT YOU'RE DRIVING AT...WE COULD LIVE OFF YOUR PROPERTY FOR YEARS! OKAY. I TAKE BACK WHAT I SAID!

OH, FRED...SUCH CRUDE HUMOR! YET....I FORGIVE YOU. I REALIZE...

...IT'S MY *CULTURE* AND *SOCIAL STANDING* ...NOT *MY MONEY* THAT ATTRACTS YOU!

ANYTHING YOU SAY JUST SO WE UNDERSTAND EACH OTHER, IF YOU LIKE TO BE *KIDDED*, I WON'T STAND IN YOUR WAY!

I LOVED YOU MADLY THEN...ALMOST AS MUCH AS I DO *NOW!* I REMEMBER AFTER WE WERE ENGAGED...

...*YOU* BROKE THAT DATE WITH ME ...

I TELL YA... I FORGOT!

AND I TELL YOU THAT YOU SNEAKED OFF TO SEE THAT *COMMON* BETTY MERRIWEATHER! DON'T TRY TO HIDE THE TRUTH FROM *ME!*

LOOK HERE, CHARLOTTE. I AGREED TO MARRY YOU, BUT I DIDN'T SIGN MYSELF OVER TO YOU LIKE A PIECE OF *PROPERTY!* YOU HAVE NO RIGHT TO *SPY* ON ME!

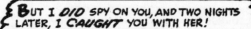

BUT I *DID* SPY ON YOU, AND TWO NIGHTS LATER, I *CAUGHT* YOU WITH HER!

SO, *THIS* IS THE APPOINTMENT YOU HAD, SOME LITTLE JOKE... AND SOME LITTLE JOKER *YOU* TURNED OUT TO BE! YOU...YOU CHEAP LIAR!

YOU GOING TO LET HER TALK THAT WAY TO YOU, FRED?

TELL HER WHAT YOU THINK OF SOMEONE WHO SPEAKS OF YOUR FIANCEE LIKE THAT, FRED!

WHY...ER...SHE... ER...DIDN'T MEAN ANYTHING, CHARLOTTE. DID--ER--DID YOU, BETTY?

HOW DARE YOU APOLOGIZE FOR HER? TELL HER WHAT YOU THINK OF HER! TELL HER THAT SHE'S A *CHEAP LITTLE HUSSY* WITH THE CHARACTER OF AN ALLEY CAT!

IS *THAT* WHAT YOU THINK OF ME, FRED?

OF COURSE YOU WERE TOO PROUD TO TELL BETTY THAT YOUR BUSINESS HAD JUST FAILED AND THAT YOU'D BE OUT ON THE STREET WITHOUT A SHIRT IF NOT FOR *MY* HELP!

WELL, FRED ...IS IT?

WHY ...ER... *TELL HER!*

YEAH, BETTY. I GUESS THAT SUMS IT UP. Y-YOU'RE JUST *NO GOOD!*

YOU SPINELESS WORM! I DON'T WANT TO SEE YOU AGAIN...EVER!

8

HOW YOU'VE CHANGED SINCE THEN, DEAR. OF COURSE, I KNEW YOUR WEAKNESSES AND I WAS WILLING TO TAKE YOU WITH THEM. THAT'S BECAUSE I *LOVED* YOU SO MUCH... AND I'VE PROVEN IT IN ALL THESE YEARS, HAVEN'T I, DARLING?

YOU DIDN'T REALIZE THE DEPTH OF MY LOVE THEN, THOUGH... REMEMBER WHAT HAPPENED WHEN BETTY LEFT?

YOU...YOU DON'T LOVE ME! YOU JUST LIKE THE FEELING OF *OWNING* ME... AS IF I WAS A FIGURE IN YOUR BANKBOOK!

THAT WAS UNKIND, FRED...AS YOU KNOW NOW. COULD ANYONE HAVE BEEN A BETTER COMPANION...MORE *UNDERSTANDING* AND *TENDER* THAN I HAVE THROUGH THESE YEARS?

THE CHAMPAGNE'S READY, AND I'LL BE RIGHT IN, DEAR! IT'S A FITTING BEVERAGE FOR THE TEN YEARS OF LOYALTY YOU'VE GIVEN ME...

...TEN YEARS THAT WE'VE DINED TOGETHER...LISTENED TO OUR FAVORITE SONGS TOGETHER... JUST THE TWO OF US SO BLISSFULLY ALONE...

YES...I NEVER DREAMED THAT YOU'D BE SO TRUE TO ME...BUT IT WAS EASY TO MANAGE...EASY TO MAKE SURE THAT YOU'D NEVER LEAVE ME.

4

FREEDOM

Martin hated her. She controlled his life completely and warped it into a horrible existence.

His life was not worth living. Yes, his wife, Ellen made it so.

But that was before he met Lois. That was before happiness was thrust out to him, and he knew he had to take it.

She was only his secretary at first. Their talk dealt only with business, and there weren't too many words that passed between them.

But one day he was looking over her shoulder; she had been typing something for him. He saw then for the first time the lovely creature she was.

He couldn't stop himself. He pulled her to him. He kissed her long and hard, and she clung to him.

"Martin," she said, "I love you."

"I love you, too, Lois," he said, and he did.

That was how it started...simply, easily. But then the tempo picked up at a furious pace. He saw her as often as was possible, and he always tried to make it possible. Still he never saw enough of Lois, and he was seeing too much of his wife, Ellen.

It was then that he found his solution. He had been doing some dealings with an amazing scientific engineer. Some of it was not too ethical, and if Martin wanted to, he could have ruined him. But he took his payment in another fashion. The engineer had been doing some great experimental work on a fantastic television set. A person at one end of the transmitter would be whipped through space and come through the screen of any television set he chose.

His experiments were still secret. And Martin took advantage of the secrecy. The plan was simple and foolproof. Martin would set up the transmitter hundreds of miles from his home. He would let his presence at this spot be known. Then he would pass through space and enter his home in a flash of a second. He would kill his wife as quickly as his gloved hands could clutch her throat, and then return through space to the transmitter.

No one would believe he had done it. They'd know he was at this spot hundreds of miles from his home.

Everything was set up. Nothing was forgotten. Martin was the happiest man in the world that evening. He would soon win his freedom, and gain his happiness.

Martin wasted no time at all. He set the transmitter. He climbed into the cock-pit like contraption. He pressed the button, and he was off into space...

But Martin never knew what happened at his house that evening. He didn't know what was going on between the engineer and his wife, Ellen. He didn't know that the engineer was at his house that evening. He didn't know the plug was pulled out of his television set.

He only knew that he had gained complete freedom forever...in space!

CHILLY
CHAMBER MUSIC

SONGS FROM THE
SPOOK BOX!

GHOUL OF MY DREAMS--
I LOVE YOU!

IT'S A CRIME...
BUT I DO!

BUT...WHEN ALL'S SAID AND DONE...
YOU HAVE THE GUN!

GHOUL OF MY DREAMS--
PLEASE HEED MY SCREAMS...

BLAM!
BLAM!

BUCKSHOT'S NO GOOD...
I DON'T WANT TO BOAST!

BUT--GHOUL OF MY DREAMS...
YOU CAN'T KILL A GHOST!

3

CAR BURNING OIL?
Engineer's Discovery Stops it Quick
Without A Cent For Mechanical Repairs!

If your car is using too much oil—if it is sluggish, hard to start, slow on pickup, lacks pep and power—you are paying good money for oil that's burning up in your engine instead of providing lubrication. Why? Because your engine is leaking. Friction has worn a gap between pistons and cylinder wall. Oil is pumping up into the combustion chamber, fouling your motor with carbon. Gas is exploding down through this gap, going to waste.

SAVE $50 TO $150 REPAIR BILL

LIKE SQUEEZING TOOTHPASTE OUT OF A TUBE

Before you spend $50.00 to $150.00 for an engine overhaul, read how you can fix that leaky engine yourself, in just a few minutes, without buying a single new part, without even taking your engine down. It's almost as easy as squeezing toothpaste or shaving cream out of a tube, thanks to the discovery of a new miracle substance called Power Seal. This revolutionary, new compound combines the *lubricating* qualities of Moly, the "greasy" wonder metal, with the leak-sealing properties of Vermiculite, the mineral product whose particles *expand* under heat. (Up to 30 times original size.)

Just squeeze Power-Seal out of the tube into your motor's cylinders through the spark plug openings. It will spread over pistons, piston rings and cylinder walls as your engine runs and it will PLATE every surface with a smooth, shiny, metallic film *that won't come off!* No amount of pressure can scrape it off. No amount of heat can break it down. It fills the cracks, scratches and scorings caused by engine wear. It closes the gap between worn piston rings and cylinders with an automatic self-expanding seal that stops oil pumping, stops gas blow-by and restores compression. No more piston slapping, no more engine knocks. You get more power, speed, mileage.

This genuine plating is self-lubricating too for Moly, the greasy metal lubricant, reduces friction as nothing else can! It is the only lubricant indestructible enough to be used in U. S. atomic energy plants and jet engines. It never drains down, never leaves your engine dry. Even after your car has been standing for weeks, even in coldest weather, you can start it in a flash, because the lubrication is in the metal itself. That's why you'll need amazingly little oil; you'll get hundreds, even thousands of more miles per quart.

TRY IT FREE!

You don't risk a penny. Prove to yourself that Power-Seal will make your car run like new. Put it in your engine on 30 days' Free Trial. If you are not getting better performance out of your car than you thought possible—if you have not stopped oil burning and have not increased gas mileage—return the empty tube and get your money back in full. Power-Seal is absolutely harmless; it cannot hurt the finest car in any way. It can only preserve and protect your motor.

RUDSON AUTOMOTIVE INDUSTRIES

400 Madison Ave.   Dept. H C-7
New York 17, N.Y.

POWER SEAL MAKES WORN OUT TAXI ENGINE RUN LIKE NEW

Here are the Test Engineer's notarized figures showing the sensational increase in compression obtained in a 1950 De Soto taxi that had run for 93,086 miles. Just one POWER SEAL injection increased pep and power, reduced gas consumption, cut oil burning nearly 50%.

	Cyl. 1	Cyl. 2	Cyl. 3	Cyl. 4	Cyl. 5	Cyl. 6
BEFORE	90 lbs.	90 lbs.	105 lbs.	90 lbs.	80 lbs.	100 lbs.
AFTER	115 lbs.	115 lbs.	117 lbs.	115 lbs.	115 lbs.	115 lbs.

BEST INVESTMENT WE EVER MADE, SAYS DRIVER-OWNER

"We simply inserted the POWER SEAL per instructions and made no other repairs or adjustments. Compression readings were taken before and after and showed a big improvement in both cars. As a result the engine gained a lot more pick-up and power which was especially noticeable on hills. What impressed us most was the sharp reduction in oil consumption. In one cab, we've actually been saving a quart a day and figure we have saved $11.20 on oil alone since the POWER SEAL was applied a month ago. In the other cab, oil consumption was cut practically in half. We have also been getting better gas mileage. All in all, POWER SEAL turned out to be just about the best investment we ever made. It paid for itself in two weeks and has been saving money for us ever since, to say nothing of postponing the cost of major overhauls that would have run into real money." *Town Taxi, Douglaston, N.Y.*

SEND NO MONEY!

Simply send the coupon and your Power-Seal injection will be sent to you at once C.O.D. plus postage and handling charges. Or, to save the postage and handling charges, simply enclose full payment with the coupon. For 6-cylinder cars order the Regular Size, only $4.95. For 8-cylinder cars order the Jumbo Size, $7.95. Power-Seal is now available only by mail from us. Send the coupon at once.

CUT! THAT WAS VERY GOOD, GARZAN! WE'LL PRINT IT!

OF COURSE YOU WILL, STEVENS! I CAN'T PRANCE HERE ALL DAY IN THIS STUPID COSTUME!

YOU WERE MAGNIFICENT, SIR!

SIMPLY GREAT!

SNIFF--SNIFF--UH-- YES! HURRY UP WITH THAT SPRAY! I FEEL A COLD COMING ON!

THAT WAS GARZAN! BUT HERE ARE SOME OF THE OTHER GARZANS!

LIGHTS CAMERA ACTION!

AND NOW BACK TO OUR FEARLESS HERO AS HE WATCHES HIS STAND-INS REPORT IN ONE AFTER ANOTHER...

MY HAND-- THINK IT'S BROKEN!

YOU'LL BE ALL RIGHT IN A FEW WEEKS! HOW WAS HE, GARZAN?

ROTTEN! HE SHOULD HAVE COME CLOSER TO THOSE CROCODILES! WE WANT REALISM IN THIS PICTURE! REALISM--LIKE THIS!

2

AYYYAYAYAYAA!

YOU SEE--? *REALISM*--IT HAS TO COME FROM THE DIAPHRAGM! HE SHOULD HAVE LET THE CROCODILES CATCH HIM FOR A MOMENT! HE *DIDN'T!* GET *RID* OF HIM!

YES! GARZAN WAS A FINICKY HERO, HE WAS ALSO VERY *VAIN!*

WELL--SINCE YOU'RE HALF-BACKER IN THIS PICTURE, WHAT WOULD *YOU* SUGGEST?

MORE STUNT-MEN WHO CAN PUT *REALISM* IN A SCENE!

PLEASE--MR. GARZAN, CAN YOU SLIP US A BUCK? I--I'M JACK SWEENEY--AND THESE ARE YOUR OTHER STUNT-MEN IN YOUR LAST FOUR PICTURES! WE NEED IT!

WHAT'S THE MATTER? CAN'T YOU GET *WORK?*

WE'RE CRIPPLED, SIR...ACCIDENTS... ON YOUR SETS--STEVE, HERE, BROKE HIS LEG DIVING OFF A CLIFF...I HURT MY BACK IN THAT GORILLA SCENE...PLEASE, WE...

TAKE YOUR HANDS OFF ME! WHY DON'T THEY KEEP YOU FOOLS OFF THIS SET?

I'LL HOLD YOU STRICTLY RESPONSIBLE FOR THOSE CANNED PRINTS, STEVENS! REMEMBER--*REALISM!* SEE YOU IN THE MORNING!

YES--IN THE MORNING...

AND THE FOLLOWING MORNING...

THAT'S ENOUGH OF THESE LOVE SCENES! MUSTN'T LET MY LIPS BECOME TOO PUFFED! I'M HAVING A BATCH OF STILLS TAKEN OF MY PROFILE FOR MY FAN CLUBS!

OKAY--I'LL TELL THE STAFF TO KNOCK OFF FOR AWHILE!

OH, NO YOU WON'T! WHAT'S WRONG WITH THE CAVE-CLIMBING SCENE? GO ON WITH THAT! HAVE YOUR FELLOW CLIMB THAT ROPE!

BUT HE CAN'T DO THAT! THE ROPE HAS TO BE REINFORCED! IT'S TOO DANGEROUS!

I'LL BOW OUT OF THIS ROTTEN PICTURE! I HAVE HALF A MIND TO DO IT NOW! GIVE ME SOME ACTION!

OKAY, MR. STEVENS! I GUESS I'M READY! DON'T WANT ANY HARD FEELINGS!

LISTEN, KID! I'LL CHUCK THIS WHOLE ASSIGNMENT DOWN THE DRAIN! THAT ROPE'S NOT STRONG ENOUGH!

NO--I'LL MAKE IT! IF WE DON'T HUMOR HIM, WE'LL ALL BE OUT OF JOBS--AND I CAN'T AFFORD TO BE!

OKAY! BUT BE CAREFUL! GET THOSE CAMERAS ROLLING! WATCH IT, KID! GO VERY SLOW!

I'VE GOT TO! MUSTN'T LOOK DOWN...

YAAAAAAAA

SNAP!

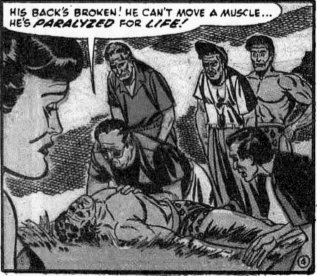

HIS BACK'S BROKEN! HE CAN'T MOVE A MUSCLE... HE'S PARALYZED FOR LIFE!

I'M SORRY! TOUGH LUCK! I'LL SEND A CHECK TO HIS FAMILY! GET THIS SET CLEANED UP-- HIRE A NEW STUNT-MAN! SEE YOU IN THE MORNING!

BUT THAT NIGHT, GARZAN HAD SOME TOUGH LUCK, TOO...

YOU'RE BARRICADING THE HIGHWAY! WHAT'S THE MEANING OF THIS?

YOU'LL SEE, MR. GARZAN! WE'RE JUST A GROUP OF YOUR FANS!

HERE! WHAT ARE YOU DOING? LET GO OF THE WHEEL! I'LL CALL THE POLICE! HELP!

SAVE YOUR GLORIOUS VOICE, SIR! WE WON'T HURT YOU! WE JUST WANT TO SPEND AN HOUR WITH YOU!

THEY DROVE THE CAR IN SILENCE. THEY TOOK HIM TO A MOVIE LOT...

Y-YOU WON'T HURT ME? YOU'LL LET ME GO?

OF COURSE WE WILL! BUT WE JUST WANT YOU TO DO US A FAVOR! HERE-- PUT ON YOUR JUNGLE CLOTHES!

AND AS GARZAN BECAME GARZAN...

DOES EVERYONE HAVE SEATS? ARE YOU SURE YOU CAN ALL SEE?

YES!

OH, YES!

W-WHY ARE YOU HANDING ME A DAGGER? Y-YOU'RE GOING TO KILL ME!

OH NO-- WE WOULDN'T DO THAT, MR. GARZAN! WE JUST WANT TO SEE YOU IN REALISTIC ACTION!

AAAIIIIIEEEE!!

MOTHERLY LOVE

"Tim," I would often tell my son, "you're not getting any younger. Why don't you get a nice, pretty young girl and settle down?"

His answer was always the same. "Mom," he'd say, "when I meet the girl that I'm really in love with, then you can be sure I'll get married."

My words just didn't work. No a-- mount of "motherly advice" would help.

There was one time I thought he was finally going to take the vows. He had been seeing Judy Davis, a girl who lived in the neighborhood. They seemed so happy together and I was sure that my son was finally getting married.

I asked Tim about it, too. And this time he didn't give me his usual answer. He just smiled, pinched my cheek, and said, "Mom, you ask too many questions!"

But all our plans were ruined a few days later. Judy had suddenly eloped with her boss.

Tim was heart-broken. And a short time later, he left my house.

The first trip to Mars was going on at that time. Tim had had some good knowledge on the scientific aspects of space travel, though he had never traveled in a rocket ship before. But in these first expeditions, he saw his chance to help our planet, gain the thrill of space exploration and forget his broken love affair.

I thought the idea was dangerous, but I didn't want to interfere. So Tim was on that very first ship that arrived in Mars.

I didn't hear much from Tim for a long time after that. Of course I received some mail from him, but his letter were short, not much newsworthy and far between.

But one happy day I received a letter which said:

"I'm coming home next month, and I think you're going to be especially happy to see me. I've got a wonderful surprise for you!"

That was all I had to read. I was sure my son had been married. Yes I would be especially happy to see him.

The month seemed to drag. But finally it was over, and the day had arrived when Tim was to come home.

I scrubbed my house over and over that day, wanting to make an impression on my son...and his wife. I looked at it ten times, not wanting to leave a corner unturned.

Then the door-bell rang, and Tim came rushing in. He took me in his arms, and as he hugged me, I noticed a roach-like insect crawl on the floor. I was ashamed, but stealthily without Tim seeing, I crushed it with my foot...

"ARRRRR!" the insect seemed to scream. And Tim pulled back with a horrible suddeness!

He shrieked, his eyes welled with tears, as he looked at the dead insect. He blurted:

"M-m-ma, sh-sh-she's a M-martian ...sh-sh-she w-w-was my w-w-wife!"

CHILLER DILLERS

HERE'S A TRICK THAT WILL ASTOUND YOU! TAKE A SHEET OF NOTE PAPER AND STRETCH IT BETWEEN TWO GLASSES, SO THAT IT FORMS A SORT OF BRIDGE. THEN...SET A THIRD GLASS ON THE BRIDGE...WITHOUT THE PAPER COLLAPSING!

THE SOLUTION TO THIS IS...PAPER-THIN! SIMPLY *PLEAT* THE PAPER LENGTHWAYS. IT WILL THEN BEAR THE WEIGHT OF THE THIRD GLASS!

I'M THE *MEDIUM*! YOUR CARD IS THE... *FIVE OF HEARTS*!

A PERSON NAMES ANY CARD IN THE PACK! SOMEONE IS SENT TO THE PHONE TO CALL UP A MIND-READER! WHEN HE COMES TO THE PHONE HE IS ASKED THE NAME OF THE CHOSEN CARD, AND HE NAMES IT IMMEDIATELY!

HERE'S HOW IT'S DONE! THE *SUIT*...OR COLOR... IS TOLD BY THE LAST NAME! THUS...A NAME BEGINNING WITH THE LETTER "A" MEANS DIAMONDS ..."B" MEANS CLUBS..."C" MEANS HEARTS...AND "D" MEANS SPADES! THE FIRST NAME...AS SEEN BELOW...IS THE NUMBER! SO...FOR THE FIVE OF HEARTS...YOUR ACCOMPLICE'S NAME WILL BE EDWARD COBB!

ACE...ARTHUR	(A)	EIGHT...HARRY	(H)
TWO...BILL	(B)	NINE...ISAAC	(I)
THREE...CHARLES	(C)	TEN...JOSEPH	(J)
FOUR...DAVID	(D)	JACK...KENT	(K)
FIVE...EDWARD	(E)	QUEEN...LOUIS	(L)
SIX...FRANK	(F)	KING...MAX	(M)
SEVEN...GEORGE	(G)	JOKER...TOM	(*)

CLINK!

PAPER IS LIGHTER THAN A HALF-DOLLAR! THAT'S A *SCIENTIFIC FACT*! BUT...CAN YOU *DISPROVE* SCIENCE...BY MAKING THE PAPER FALL AS RAPIDLY AS THE COIN?

LAY THE PAPER UPON THE COIN AND DROP THE COIN FLAT! THE PAPER WILL FALL WITH THE COIN! THE PAPER...HOWEVER...SHOULD BE *SMALLER* THAN THE COIN!

BEWARE OF THE SHOCKING TWIST THAT MUST COME FROM THIS...

BLACK PASSION

MY NAME'S JASON WILTON. I'M A GUY WHO WOULD SPEND 8 HOURS EVERY DAY IN A STUFFY OFFICE NATURALLY I WANTED TO PASS MY EVENINGS IN A GAY ATMOSPHERE BUT MY WIFE ELVIRA HAD DIFFERENT IDEAS...

WHAT MAKES YOU THINK CANDLES ON THE TABLE WILL SUBSTITUTE FOR A *NIGHTCLUB!* I'M GOING OUT!

JASON!

I DROVE OUR CAR OUT WITH THE GEARS GRINDING-- BUT I SPENT A MISERABLE EVENING...

SOMETHING WRONG, MR. WILTON?

1

BUT THEN I STARTED VISITING MY BUSINESS CLUB, AND I BEGAN TO *LIKE* IT. IT SOON BECAME MY *SECOND HOME*...

SET 'EM UP AGAIN, HARRY.

GIVE US ANOTHER ONE OF YOUR WONDERFUL STORIES, JASON!

AND HOME BECAME A PLACE WHERE *I SLEPT NIGHTS*, ELVIRA JUST THE WOMAN WHO PREPARED MY MEALS.

DON'T WAIT UP FOR ME, ELVIRA. WE'RE HAVING A POKER TOURNAMENT. I'M TEN DOLLARS AHEAD!

THEN IT HAPPENED! ONE RAINY DAY I OPENED THE DOOR OF A TAXI THAT HAD STOPPED FOR A RED LIGHT, AND I MET— *CINDY DRUE!*

I HOPE YOU DON'T MIND MY SHARING YOUR TAXI. I'M ONLY GOING TEN BLOCKS OR SO. NEVER USE MY OWN CAR WHEN IT RAINS.

NOT AT ALL.

YOU'RE A MODEL? I THOUGHT THAT BEAUTIFUL FACE WAS FAMILIAR!

YOU'RE QUITE OBSERVING AND *COMPLIMENTARY* AS WELL!

WE SOON GOT BETTER ACQUAINTED...

MR. WILTON, I SCARCELY KNOW YOU, BUT I NEVER FELT SO MUCH AT EASE WITH ANY MAN!

THE SAME GOES FOR ME— AND I PREFER FIRST NAMES — *CINDY!* MINE IS JASON.

AND A SHORT TIME LATER, SHE HAD ME GOING AROUND IN CIRCLES...IN CIRCLES OF LOVE!

JASON, HONEY— TONIGHT YOU *ARE* GOING HOME EARLY— I HAVE A MODELING APPOINTMENT EIGHT O'CLOCK TOMORROW MORNING!

I'LL GO, BUT NOT WILLINGLY.

2

NO, I COULDN'T GET ENOUGH OF HER!

I SAID TONIGHT YOU'RE STAYING HOME!

ELVIRA, GIVE ME THAT COAT. YOU'RE NOT TELLING ME WHAT TO DO!

THEN I'M GOING WITH YOU! WAIT FOR ME!

NEVER MIND THE GRACIOUS GESTURE. IT'S TOO LITTLE, TOO LATE... ANYWAY, TONIGHT I'VE GOT TO WORK!

YES, I WENT TO "WORK"...

JASON, I NEED YOU SO MUCH. I WANT TO BE WITH YOU ALWAYS! I'LL QUIT MY JOB, WE'LL GO AWAY, TOGETHER, TO SOME ROMANTIC PLACE!

KISS ME AGAIN, CINDY!

PASSION SHORTENS THE HOURS AND IT WAS LATE WHEN I GOT HOME. I TIPTOED IN QUIETLY. THERE WERE LESS ARGUMENTS THAT WAY.

AWFULLY QUIET. I HOPE SHE'S SOUND ASLEEP.

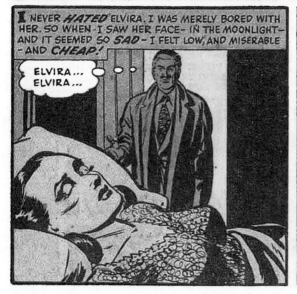

I NEVER HATED ELVIRA, I WAS MERELY BORED WITH HER. SO WHEN I SAW HER FACE - IN THE MOONLIGHT - AND IT SEEMED SO SAD - I FELT LOW, AND MISERABLE - AND CHEAP!

ELVIRA... ELVIRA...

WHAT A FOOL I'VE BEEN. NO MAN HAD A MORE FAITHFUL WIFE, AND I TREAT HER SO SHABBILY. I'LL SEE CINDY TOMORROW AND TELL HER WE'RE THROUGH! ELVIRA AND I WILL BE HAPPY AGAIN!

3

I EXPECTED A LONG AND HECTIC EVENING WITH CINDY, SO I MADE AN EXCUSE TO ELVIRA, JUST IN CASE. I WAS PROUD OF ELVIRA'S CONSIDERATION AND UNDERSTANDING...

OF COURSE, DEAR, FINISH YOUR WORK AND THEN RELAX AT THE CLUB AS LONG AS YOU LIKE. I'LL READ A LITTLE AND GO TO BED EARLY.

I'LL TRY NOT TO BE *TOO LATE,* DARLING!

IT WAS JUST AS I EXPECTED...

CINDY, I'M NOT SEEING YOU AFTER TONIGHT!

WHAT?

DON'T JOKE WITH *ME!*

IT'S NO JOKE. I'VE KEPT SOMETHING FROM YOU. I'M *MARRIED!* I'VE JUST REALIZED WHAT A *FOOL* I'VE BEEN AND I'M GOING *BACK* TO MY WIFE!

JUST LIKE THAT, EH? ALL RIGHT -- I'LL PLAY ALONG WITH YOU -- FOR A SLIGHT TOKEN OF *AFFECTION* -- SOMETHING TO *FORGET* YOU -- SAY *$5,000?*

$5,000? ARE YOU *MAD?* WHAT DO YOU TAKE ME FOR?

JUST WHAT YOU TOOK ME FOR -- A *SUCKER!* IF I DON'T GET THAT FIVE GRAND I'LL TELL YOUR WIFE WHAT A *"LOVING"* HUSBAND YOU'VE BEEN!

IT WAS RAW *BLACKMAIL!* SHE SNEERED AT ME. I PLEADED WITH HER. SHE LAUGHED IN MY FACE. THEN MY HANDS - I COULDN'T STOP THEM - MY HANDS, THEY --

YOU'RE CHOKING ME - JASON! *AAGH...*

SHE WAS *DEAD... VERY DEAD!* I WAS FRANTIC WITH FEAR, AND YET I WORKED WITH THE CALM OF A *PROFESSIONAL* MURDERER! I COVERED HER BODY WITH A BLANKET...THE FIRE ESCAPE LED TO AN ALLEY...

THANK GOODNESS NO ONE SAW ME...

I TOOK HER INTO THE CAR...

THE *CLIFFS* OVERLOOKING THE RIVER! THAT'S WHERE I'LL TAKE HER!

I WRAPPED HER IN HEAVY TIRE CHAINS SO SHE'D SINK TO THE BOTTOM OF THE RIVER, AND MY *SECRET* WOULD STAY THERE WITH HER!

POOR ELVIRA. PROBABLY WONDERING WHEN I'LL BE HOME. I'M NOT *WORTHY* OF HER TRUST— BUT I'LL MAKE IT UP TO HER! I'LL GIVE HER THE *UNDERSTANDING* SHE DESERVES, I *SWEAR* IT!

I DROVE THE CAR INTO THE CARPORT BESIDE OUR HOME. A LAMP WAS LIT IN THE LIVING ROOM. NO DOUBT SHE WAS READING, I OPENED THE DOOR SLIGHTLY. THERE WAS ELVIRA WITH A STRANGER BENDING OVER HER. AT FIRST I THOUGHT SHE HAD BEEN HURT...

BUT THEN I KNEW WHAT HAD HAPPENED...

LET'S RUN AWAY, ELVIRA DARLING!

YES, YES...WHENEVER YOU SAY... NOW!

THE END.

5

Borrow Money BY MAIL!

ON YOUR OWN SIGNATURE

Our Guarantee If for any reason you return the money within 10 days after the loan is made there will be no charge or cost to you.

ANY AMOUNT
$50.00 to $600.00

Quick – Easy – Private – Confidential

No Matter Where You Live in the U. S.—You Can Borrow from State Finance
No Endorsers or Co-Signers Needed — Complete Privacy Assured!

So much easier than calling on friends and relatives ... so much more business-like ... to borrow the money you need BY MAIL from fifty-year old State Finance Company. No matter where you live in the U. S., you can borrow any amount from $50.00 to $600.00 *entirely by mail in complete privacy* without asking anyone to co-sign or endorse your loan. Friends, neighbors, employer ... will NOT know you are applying for a loan. Convenient monthly budget payments. If loan is repaid ahead of time, you pay ONLY for the time you actually use the money! If you are over 25 years of age and steadily employed, simply mail the coupon below for your FREE Loan Application and Loan Papers. State amount you want to borrow. *Everything you need to make a loan by return mail will be sent to you in a plain envelope!* So mail the coupon below today!

Thousands of Men and Women Like Yourself Use Our
Confidential By-Mail Loan Service

Repay in Convenient Monthly Installments

Monthly payments are made to fit your budget best. You can start paying six weeks after the loan is made, and repay in convenient monthly payments out of your future earnings. The cost of the loan is regulated by the laws of the State of Nebraska. For example, if the loan is repaid ahead of time, you pay only for the time you use the money ... not one day longer! One out of three applicants get cash on their signature only. Furniture and auto loans are also made. No matter in which state you live, you can borrow from State Finance Company in complete confidence.

Clip and Mail Coupon Below for Fast Action

FREE LOAN PAPERS
NO OBLIGATION

If you are over 25 years of age and steadily employed, simply mail the coupon below for your Loan Application, sent to you in a plain envelope. There is no obligation, and you'll get fast action. You can get the money you need to help pay bills, to buy furniture, to repair your home or car, to pay doctor or hospital bills, to pay for a vacation, a trip, or for schooling, or for any other purpose. This money is here, waiting for you, so rush this coupon today!

CONFIDENTIAL

Complete privacy is assured. No one knows you are applying for a loan. All details are handled in the privacy of your own home, and entirely by mail. ONLY YOU AND WE KNOW ABOUT IT!

IMPORTANT

You must be at least 25 years old to borrow by mail from State Finance.

Old Reliable Company —
MORE THAN 50 YEARS OF SERVICE

STATE FINANCE COMPANY was organized in 1897. During the past 54 years, we have helped over 1,000,000 men and women in all walks of life. Confidential loans are made all over America, in all 48 states. We are licensed by the Banking Department of the State of Nebraska to do business under the Small Loan Law.

You'll enjoy borrowing this easy, confidential, convenient way from this old, responsible company in whom you can place the greatest confidence.

STATE FINANCE COMPANY   MAIL COUPON TODAY!
Dept. F-143, 323 Securities Bldg., Omaha 2, Nebr.

Without obligation rush full details in plain envelope, with FREE Loan Application and Loan Papers for my signature, if I decide to borrow.

Name..

Address......................................

City.........................State............

Occupation..........................Age........

Amount you want to borrow $.........

STATE FINANCE COMPANY

Dept. F-143, 323 Securities Bldg.
Omaha 2, Nebraska

CHAMBER OF CHILLS MAGAZINE, NOVEMBER, 1953, Vol. 1, No. 20, IS PUBLISHED BI-MONTHLY by WITCHES TALES, INC., 1860 Broadway, New York 23, N.Y. Entered as second class matter at the Post Office at New York, N.Y. under the Act of March 3, 1879. Single copies 10c. Subscription rates, 10 issues for $1.00 in the U.S. and possessions, elsewhere $1.50. All names in this periodical are entirely fictitious and no identification with actual persons is intended. Contents copyrighted, 1953, by Witches Tales, Inc., New York City. Printed in the U.S.A. Title Registered in U. S. Patent Office.

The tops in horror brings you once again a trail of endless suspense! CHAMBER OF CHILLS, a terror mag with the shock touch, opens its doors to the newest treat in terror!

Here we have an assortment of stories designed for electrifying impact. Every one has been built on the geometric plane of horror, well-calculated to keep you in suspense from start to the shocking finish!

Every tick of THE CLOCK runs off an experience in clashing, mind-searing thoughts...where every cog wheel meshes with evil!

An attempt at MURDER fills the package for death. It is the frantic account of a man possessed with evil, but caught in its web!

A recluse, caught in the web of the shadows he calls home, suddenly is confronted with a Martian. This is the meat of LAY THAT PISTOL DOWN, a science-fiction saga that rocks the heavens!

You'll be trapped in a horror unlimited that rocks with frantic fury till you reach the END OF THE LINE!

But now is the time for the unknown, the time to face shocking suspense that waits in the CHAMBER OF CHILLS!

CHAMBER OF CHILLS — Contents NO. 20

THE CLOCK

THAT'S THE CLOCK, ALL RIGHT! THE CLOCK THAT STARTED IT ALL... THAT TOOK RACHEL'S *LIFE!*

TICK TOCK

I'M A CLOCKMAKER... ONE OF THE BEST IN TOWN! BUT I WAS ALSO A HUSBAND WHO WAS VERY MUCH IN LOVE. RACHEL THERE-- WAS MY WIFE!

SHE'S NOT PRETTY TO LOOK AT NOW,... LIKE MY CLOCK,. BUT SHE *USED* TO BE! RACHEL WAS THE *WORLD* TO *ME!* GUESS NO HARM IN TELLING YOU-- WHAT WITH THE CLOCK ALL FINISHED NOW... I LOVED HER WITH MY *HEART.* AND *SOUL!*

TICK TOCK TOCK TOCK TICK

RACHEL AND I SHARED THE LOVE OF OUR CLOCK SHOP. HOW WE LOVED IT!

JUST THINK, DARLING! AFTER *FIFTEEN YEARS,* WE'RE STILL NOT BORED WITH OUR LIVES! YOU LOVE ME-- DON'T YOU?

OF COURSE I DO, HONEY! THAT'S WHY I SPEND ALL DAY IN MY WORK-SHOP HERE! EVERY-THING I MAKE-- I MAKE FOR *YOU!* I JUST ATTACHED THE TIME-SPRING! LISTEN!

TICK·· TOCK·· TICK·· TOCK·· TICK!

2

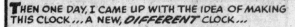

THEN ONE DAY, I CAME UP WITH THE IDEA OF MAKING THIS CLOCK....A NEW, *DIFFERENT* CLOCK...

CAL, DEAR...YOUR SUPPER IS GETTING COLD! PLEASE PUT DOWN YOUR WORK FOR A MOMENT AND COME INSIDE!

WAIT--JUST A FEW MORE MINUTES...THIS COIL-SPRING BELONGS HERE--AND I CAN PUT ANOTHER SMALL ROD THERE...

I STARTED ON IT, GETTING THE PIECES TOGETHER, DESIGNING IT--THINKING IT OUT--*FORMING* IT! IT TOOK UP MOST OF MY TIME...

WILL YOU *PLEASE* COME TO BED? IT'S ALMOST FOUR IN THE MORNING! HOW CAN YOU WORK SO MUCH?

SHH--DON'T BOTHER ME NOW! THIS IS VERY *IMPORTANT!* GO BACK TO BED, RACHEL!

AT FIRST, RACHEL DIDN'T MIND. SHE WENT ALONG WITH IT. BUT AS MY TIME GOT TO BE TAKEN UP WITH THE CLOCK, MY ATTENTION TOWARDS RACHEL BECAME SO MUCH THE LESS...

IT'S GOING TO BE THE *BEST* CLOCK IN TOWN! EVERYONE WILL POINT TO IT AND SAY THAT *CAL STEVENS* MADE IT!

YES--AT THE *EXPENSE* OF HIS *WIFE!*

IT BEGAN TO AFFECT HER. SHE GOT MAD. HER ATTITUDE BEGAN TO CHANGE. DESPITE THIS, I STILL PAID MORE ATTENTION TO THE CLOCK...

YOU NEVER HELP ME AROUND THE HOUSE ANYMORE! YOU NEVER FIX THINGS THAT *NEED* FIXING! NOBODY GAVE YOU AN ORDER FOR THAT CLOCK! WHERE'S OUR MONEY GOING TO COME FROM?

YUP...NEARLY FINISHED WITH THIS THING, HUH? WHAT'S THAT, RACHEL?

THINGS GOT WORSE! THE MORE I PROGRESSED TOWARD THE COMPLETION OF THE CLOCK, THE LESS I SHOWED ANY OUTWARD SIGNS OF LOVE TOWARDS RACHEL...

WE COULD GO TO THAT MOVIE IN TOWN IF WE HURRY, CAL, *PLEASE*--JUST FOR *TONIGHT!* STOP WORKING ON THAT HORRIBLE CLOCK! *PLEASE!*

CAN'T, RACHEL-- I'M ALMOST THROUGH! *WAIT* TILL YOU *HEAR* IT *CHIME!* RIGHT PRETTY IT IS! RIGHT PRETTY!

THAT'S THE LAST STRAW! I'M NOT PUTTING UP WITH YOUR STUBBORNESS ANY LONGER! YOU'RE *NOT* GOING TO WORK ON THAT CLOCK!

PLEASE, DEAR... TEMPER...TEMPER ...YOU'LL FEEL BETTER IN THE MORNING! WAIT TILL YOU SEE IT! I JUST PAINTED IT AND, I--

3

I *DIDN'T WANT* RACHEL *TO DIE.* I JUST WANTED TO STOP HER--THAT'S ALL! BUT RACHEL DOESN'T BREATHE ANYMORE, SHE DOESN'T KISS ME ANYMORE! SHE DOESN'T GET ANGRY AT ME! SO I HAD TO MAKE SOME *CHANGES* ON THE CLOCK...

THERE IT IS--THE CLOCK THAT STARTED IT ALL! MY *PRETTY CLOCK!*

TICK TICK TOCK

IF RACHEL COULD SEE THE CLOCK--IN ITS PERFECTION! IF SHE COULD SEE IT WORK AS ONLY *I* COULD MAKE IT WORK!

HEAR IT? IT'S SO PRECISE! THAT'S *MY* WORK! BUT RACHEL WAS JEALOUS OF IT, POOR DEAR! ONLY-- SHE'S DEAD NOW--SO IT DOESN'T MATTER! THE CHANGES WILL TAKE CARE OF EVERYTHING...YES I'VE *REALLY* MADE A CLOCK!

TICKTOCK

TICKTOCK

POOR RACHEL...I ONLY *MEANT* TO *STOP* HER! SHE'LL HAVE TO *KNOW* THAT! HEAR IT? THREE SECONDS...

TICKTOCK TICK TOCK

TICK

...ONE SECOND... I'M COMING, RACHEL!

TOCK

BLLLAAAAAMMM!!

The End

Murderer AT LARGE

"Don't worry, Mom. Everything will be all right. I'll be through in another few minutes anyhow." Eloise smiled into the phone, as if her mother could see her calmness.

"Please don't worry, Mom," she continued. "The murderer isn't going to strike here. Besides Mr. Stewart will protect me."

She winked at Mr. Stewart, the building's janitor as he swept the office.

Mr. Stewart whispered back: "Don't know how much help I could be."

"OK, Mom," said Eloise into the phone, "see you soon."

She hung up the phone then and said to Mr. Stewart, "Gads, that murderer is getting everyone excited. How many times have I had to stay late at the office, and no one would even call. Now, my mother calls three times!"

"Maybe she's got a reason," said Mr. Stewart still sweeping away.

"Don't tell me you're worried about that murderer?" Eloise laughed.

"Five murders ain't to be sneezed at," said Mr. Stewart. "But it's you who should be worried . . . only likes girls, you know."

"Oh, Mr. Stewart, don't you pay any attention to those scare headlines in the papers. It doesn't mean a thing."

Mr. Stewart stopped his sweeping. "Young lady," he said. "I don't make myself out to be a brainy man — else I wouldn't be working here — but if I was your mother I don't think I'd be allowing you to be working late at the office!"

"Mr. Stew —"

Eloise was interrupted by a . . .

SWOOSHH! at the window.

"What's that?" shouted Mr. Stewart.

They turned around and saw . . .

"Just a piece of paper," smiled Eloise. "Gosh, Mr. Stewart, you're all bumped up with goose-pimples. Like you said, you have no reason to be afraid. The big, bad murderer only kills women!"

"I guess I'm afraid . . . for you."

Eloise had to laugh. "You're awfully sweet," she said. "I believe you really are afraid for me. But you don't have to. I don't even give this murderer a second thought."

Mr. Stewart looked at her with a strong steady stare. "You know," he said, "you can never tell who this murderer might be . . . it might even be me!"

Eloise was startled for a second. Then she chuckled. "But you really aren't," she said, "are you?"

"I don't know," he answered casually.

Still Eloise didn't seem excited. "You know," she said, "it could even be me!"

Mr. Stewart didn't say another word. He finished his sweeping and strolled silently from the room.

A few minutes later, Eloise cleaned off her desk, gathered her things together and walked out of the office. She walked down the stairs and passed Mr. Stewart in the lobby.

Then there were screams!

COME ON-A-MY HOUSE...
TO MY HOUSE-A-COME ON...

I'M-A-GONNA GIVE YOU
PLENTY OF LOVIN'
WHEN THE LIGHT'S ALL GONE!

BUT YOU'RE GONNA SCREAM AND HOLLER....
AND NOBODY'S GONNA CALL YOU "LIAR"!...

'CAUSE WHEN YOU COME ON-A-MY HOUSE
YOU'RE GONNA LOOK AT A REAL VAMPIRE!

MUUU-UU-LE TRAIN...
YAAAAAAAA!

GIT ALONG THERE...
YOU SON OF A BOW-LEGGED COW...

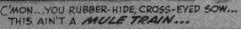

C'MON...YOU RUBBER-HIDE, CROSS-EYED SOW...
THIS AIN'T A MULE TRAIN...

YAAAAAAA!
IT'S A...GHOUL TRAIN!

THE BOOMERANG OF ALL DEATHS IS...
MURDER

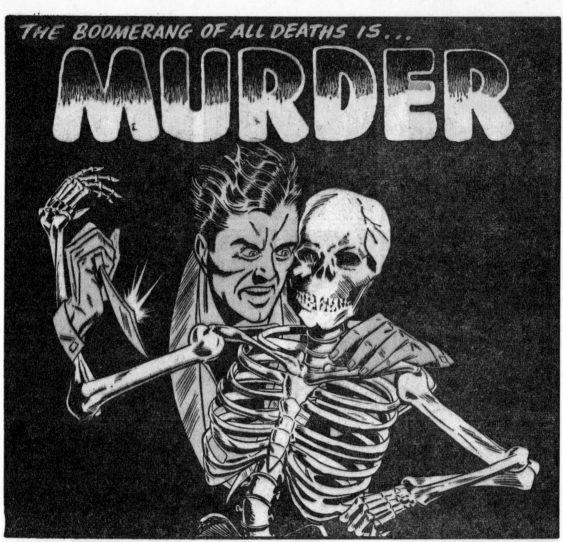

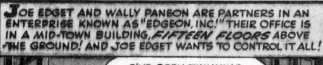

JOE EDGET AND WALLY PANEON ARE PARTNERS IN AN ENTERPRISE KNOWN AS "EDGEON, INC.!" THEIR OFFICE IS IN A MID-TOWN BUILDING, *FIFTEEN FLOORS* ABOVE THE GROUND! AND JOE EDGET WANTS TO CONTROL IT ALL!

I'VE BEEN THINKING ABOUT THAT DEAL, JOE! I *LIKE* IT!

ALL WE GOT TO DO IS CALL THE RIGHT PEOPLE ...AND WE'RE IN!

HE'LL FALL... WITH A *PUSH!*

JUST... A *LITTLE* CLOSER!

YEP, JOE... EVERYTHING IS *FINE!*

WE'LL BE RICH SOMEDAY, JOE! I'VE GOT NO DOUBTS ABOUT IT!

BUT, IT'LL ALL BE *MINE,* WALLY!

B-B-RRRING

JOE EDGET'S ATTEMPT AT MURDER WAS HALTED BY THE *PHONE!* HIS ONCE-CALM CRIMINAL ATTITUDE WAS SHOCKED INTO NERVOUSNESS!

EXCUSE ME, JOE!

YEAH-- YEAH, SURE! GO AHEAD, WALLY!

HEY, JOE... WHAT ABOUT A WEEK-END AT FISHING! I GOT THE SPORTING GOODS STORE ON THE LINE! WE COULD MAKE IT A *REAL VACATION!* WHAT ABOUT IT, JOE?

SOUNDS GOOD TO ME, WALLY! I--I'M FOR IT!

USUALLY, SATURDAY BEGINS A WEEK-END. JOE EDGET THINKS THAT IT WAS LATE FRIDAY NIGHT OR EARLY THE NEXT MORNING THAT HE THOUGHT OF MURDERING WALLY PANEON AGAIN! ANYHOW, BOTH WERE IN THE WOODS!

THE TROUT'S FINE AROUND HERE! WE'LL TAKE A CANOE ...AND TRY THE STREAM JUST BY THE NEXT BEND!

YEAH! A *CANOE'LL* BE GREAT!

IT'S DEAD IN THIS NECK OF THE WOODS! I CAN KILL HIM AND *NOBODY* WOULD KNOW! A SIMPLE *"ACCIDENT"*...

2

WALLY AND JOE RENTED A CANOE. WALLY SAID THE FISHING MIGHT BE BETTER UPSTREAM AND THEY PADDLED THERE. THE CANOE CUT THROUGH THE WATER LIKE A RAZOR...

TAKE IT EASY, JOE! I CAN'T SWIM, YOU 'KNOW!

I KNOW IT, WALLY! BUT... YOU'LL *NEVER LEARN HOW TO!*

AND... YOU'LL NEVER KNOW WHAT *HIT* YOU!

HEY, THEAH!

OVEH *HEAH*, WATER'S CALMER! FISHIN' IS REAL GOOD! HOW YE BEEN DOIN'?

JOE EDGET WAS STOPPED AGAIN. IT WAS A BABBLING GEEZER...SOME GUY WHO SEEMED TO STEP INTO THE PICTURE FROM NOWHERE! HE WAS ENOUGH, THOUGH, ENOUGH TO STOP ANY *FURTHER ATTEMPT!*

HAVEN'T STARTED YET! WE WERE JUST HEADING UPSTREAM!

PRETTY GOOD UP THERE, TOO! DON'T USE WORMS! AIN'T NO GOOD FOR TROUT! TRY PIECE O' BACON RIND!

3

SATURDAY PASSED INTO SUNDAY! IT WAS TIME TO GO...

IT WAS RESTFUL, JOE! I'M SORRY IT'S OVER. BUT... TONIGHT WE GOT THAT *PARTY* AT PETE'S HOUSE!

YEAH! ALMOST FORGOT ABOUT *THAT!* I'LL MEET YOU THERE!

LATER....

THE WHOLE WEEK-END... *SHOT!* I'LL *NEVER* GET ANOTHER CHANCE!

NAW! OPPORTUNITY'LL KNOCK AGAIN! MAYBE... AT *PETE'S PARTY!*

THE PROCESS OF DRESSING WAS OVER. JOE EDGET ARRIVED AT PETE'S HOUSE. THE MUFFLED SOUNDS OF THE PARTY CAME TO HIM BUT HE WAS STILL PONDERING HIS PARTNER'S ONCOMING *MURDER!*

I'VE GOT TO FIGURE OUT A WAY...

I -- HOLD IT! *THIS* IS WALLY'S *CAR!* IF I COULD JUST TINKER WITH THE BRAKES... A SLIGHT ADJUSTMENT COULD SEND IT ROLLING!

AS JOE EDGET WALKED TO THE PARTY, HE WAS IN GOOD SPIRITS. HE WAS STIMULATED BY THE THOUGHT OF *MURDER!* WALLY PANEON WAS STIMULATED BY *SOMETHING ELSE!*

HIYA, JOEY BABY! YOU'RE A LITTLE LATE... BUT HERE'S ONE TO CATCH UP!

THANKS, WALLY! I NEED IT!

DOWN THE HATCH, LAD! SIP N' SUP... AND DRINK IT UP! NOTHIN' LIKE A LITTLE *HOT CHOCOLATE* TO CURL YOUR TOES, EH? HA! HA!

4

SOON AFTERWARDS, JOE EDGET QUIETLY LEFT THE PARTY...OR HE WAS TRYING TO LEAVE IT...

WHERE Y' GOING, JOE?

I'LL BE BACK IN A MINUTE, HONEY! LEFT MY CIGARETTE LIGHTER IN THE CAR!

AT WALLY PANEON'S CAR...

NOW...TO TAMPER WITH THE BRAKE DRUM...

WHEN...WALLY LEAVES...HE'LL BE FEELING HIGH! HE'LL SPEED...THE BRAKES WON'T HOLD...AND...BIFF! *THE END!*

JOE EDGET MANIPULATED. EVERYTHING WAS GOING RIGHT. A SPECK DROPPED DOWN FROM THE UNDERCARRIAGE OF THE CAR AND AS HE TURNED HIS HEAD, HE SAW...

WHA?!! SOMEBODY'S...*WATCHING ME!*

JOE SLID OUT AND CAME FACE-TO-FACE WITH *WALLY PANEON!*

HELLO, JOE-- WHAT D'YA KNOW? THOUGHT I'D COME OUT AND SEE HOW THINGS WERE, JOE! PLEASANT EVENING, ISN'T IT?

YEAH, WALLY...YEAH...

GEE, JOE, YOU SHOULDN'T WORRY YOURSELF ABOUT MY CAR LIKE THAT.

I-I W-WAS JUST FIXING IT, WALLY. THAT'S ALL I WAS DOING!

I KNOW, JOE. BUT FORGET IT-- FORGET EVERYTHING! YOU AIN'T GOING TO BE WITH US MUCH LONGER! THERE WAS A LITTLE POISON IN THAT DRINK OF YOURS...THAT'LL LEAVE OUR BUSINESS JUST TO ME!

NO-- NOOOOO!

THE END

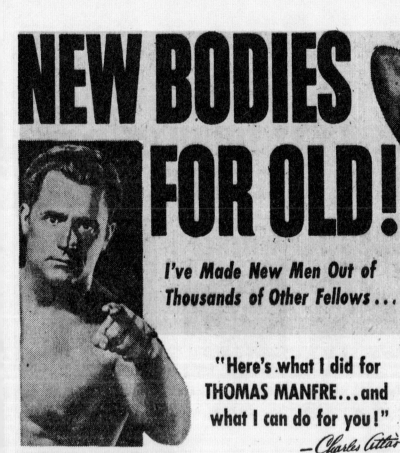

IT DIDN'T SHOUT OR SCREAM WHEN IT SAID...

LAY THAT PISTOL DOWN

TEDDY CUMMINS LIVED AT 11 VANDERNOOK AVENUE. A VERY EXCLUSIVE *ADDRESS*...AND A VERY EXCLUSIVE *HOUSE*...EVEN IF THE ARCHITECTURE WAS RATHER *GRIM* AND *OLD FASHIONED!*

TO "*NORMAL*" PEOPLE, TEDDY CUMMINS WAS SLIGHTLY ECCENTRIC. TO TEDDY, HIMSELF, HE WAS A MAN WHO JUST LIKED TO BE *ALONE*, AWAY FROM THE HUM-DRUM ACTIVITIES OF EVERYDAY LIFE! POLITE SOCIETY CALLED HIM A *RECLUSE!*

AND IN THE VAST CONFINES OF HIS CELLAR, TEDDY ACCUMULATED IN MUSTY ABUNDANCE...EVEN *OVERABUNDANCE*...WHAT HE CONSIDERED *IMPORTANT!* THERE WAS NO RHYME OR REASON TO THE STORAGE! IT BEGAN WITH *EVERYTHING*...AND STOPPED AT *NOTHING!*

LOVELY OLD NEWSPAPERS ...TO BE PUT AWAY! HEE...HEE!

THERE WERE BROKEN TOYS, WHEELS, SCRAPS OF IRON AND STEEL...AND RUBBER AND CARDBOARD! IN SHORT, ANYTHING HE COULD SALVAGE FROM THE CITY'S MOST ARISTOCRATIC GARBAGE CANS!

IT'S *SO NICE* TO *SAVE!*

AT NIGHT WHEN THE CITY SLEPT TEDDY WOULD TRAVEL FROM HOUSE TO HOUSE, PICKING THE BONES OF THE CITY'S REFUSE! HE WAS *INDUSTRIOUS* AS WELL AS ODD!

AH--THIS WILL DO! IT WILL DO, INDEED!

BUT PEOPLE GOT USED TO THE ECCENTRIC RECLUSE, AS HE BLENDED QUIETLY INTO THE BACKGROUND OF THE BUSY CITY, TROUBLING NO ONE, UNTROUBLED HIMSELF ...

HE'S QUEER, ALL RIGHT! BUT *HARMLESS.* EVERYONE'S GOT HIS FUNNY POINTS! I LIKE POTATO CHIPS WITH ICE CREAM ...HE LIKES TO *LIVE* IN A *CELLAR* FULL OF *JUNK!*

THAT'S WHAT I SAY! *LIVE AN' LET LIVE!*

TEDDY, HOWEVER, WAS NOT SO TOLERANT. THE *SLIGHTEST SOUND,* THE *FAINTEST FINGER* OF PROBING LIGHT WAS ENOUGH TO SEND HIM SCURRYING INTO A *DARK CORNER!*

HOW I ...*DETEST* THE DAYTIME!

FOR...IT WAS AT NIGHT THAT TEDDY CUMMINS DID HIS BEST WORK! AND IT WAS AT NIGHT WHEN *SOMEONE* CALLED...SOMEONE WHO DROPPED FROM *NOWHERE!*

MAGAZINES OVER HERE...

2

TOYS OVER HERE. HAVE TO KEEP EVERYTHING ORDERLY!

SUDDENLY...

STAY WHERE YOU ARE! DON'T MAKE A MOVE!

WH- WHO ARE YOU? WH-- WHAT ARE YOU DOING HERE?

YOU WOULDN'T BELIEVE ME IF I TOLD YOU... BUT I'LL TELL YOU ANYWAY. MY NAME IS GODRYLL. I CAME BY SPACE SHIP FROM MARS! WE'VE DECIDED THAT EARTH HAS POSSIBILITIES, AND I'VE BEEN SENT AS...AH...AN OBSERVOR!

TEDDY'S EQUILIBRIUM WAS UPSET! HIS APPLE CART OF PRIVACY WAS OVERTURNED BY THIS UNWANTED, UN-EARTHLY INTRUDER! HE WAS NOT GOING TO STAND FOR IT!

YOU...YOU'RE CRAZY! GET OUT! I--I DON'T LIKE PEOPLE HERE!

PUT THAT DOWN, YOU FOOL! I'M NOT READY TO KILL YOU!

BUT... BUT I'M READY TO....HA-HA-HA! HAVE A LIGHT!

KLIKK!

YOU...YOU IMBECILE! NO MORE STUNTS LIKE THAT! THERE ARE IMPORTANT ISSUES AT STAKE AND RIGHT NOW YOU ARE VALUABLE TO ME ALIVE!

3

HOW EASY IT WILL BE TO HIDE IN THIS CELLAR, UN-OBSERVED AND UNSUSPECTED. THEN AFTER I HAVE LEARNED YOUR WAYS, WHO WILL TELL THE *DIFFERENCE* BETWEEN TWO MEN WHO *LIVE* IN THE *SHADOWS?*

BUT, TEDDY *COULD* TELL THE DIFFERENCE! THAT WAS ENOUGH FOR HIM!

YOU...YOU *THING!* I WON'T *LET* YOU KILL ME!

GET OUT ...OR I *SHOOT!*

YOU *IMBECILE!* IF YOU FORCE MY HAND, I'LL *HAVE* TO KILL YOU NOW!

HEEE-HEEE-HEEE!

WH-WHAT? *WATER?* ENOUGH OF YOUR *GAMES!*

IF IT WAS A GAME, TEDDY HAD TO PLAY, HE HAD NO CHOICE! HE KNEW THAT THERE WERE NO TIES IN THE GAME OF LIFE OR DEATH... AND THERE'S ONLY *ONE* WINNER!

HA-HA! SCARED YOU, DIDN'T I?

BOIING!

WATER PISTOLS...GUNS THAT SHOOT SPARKS AND FLAGS! THE *MAN* IS *DEMENTED!*

RAT-A-TAT

TAT TAT

4

The TALKER

"Stop your idiotic blabbering! What do you know about politics?" Larz Thomas' booming voice burst forth with venom at his son, William.

"I guess I don't know much," said William. His eyes stared coldly at the man who was his father.

The guests in the Thomas' living room looked on with wild-eyed interest. They had seen similar scenes to this before. But they were always fascinated by the hate that lived in Larz Thomas.

"I guess I shouldn't talk unless I'm spoken to," said William calmly.

"You can say that again!" said Larz. "You're twenty now, yet you've still got a mind of a four-year-old! You don't know politics . . . you don't know people . . . you don't know life! You'd do a favor for the whole world if you just shut up!"

"You've never liked anything I've said, have you, Dad?"

"No! I can't remember a single instance when I liked to hear your voice! I can't even stand the way it sounds!"

The guests were becoming wary. But no one was sure what to do. Finally, someone said:

"OK, you two. Let's forget it for now. This is a party, so let's make like one!"

Larz Thomas walked away with his guests. He pasted a smile on his face and was already telling a funny story

William Thomas stayed behind. His eyes followed his father and the guests as they walked out of the room. Then he stared down at the plushy carpet and his mind moved back over the years.

He remembered his days as a child. He remembered how his father would stop his normal child questionings. Then he remembered the sound-proof room his father had built for him, the room he'd be locked into if he spoke too much, the room where he'd cry endlessly and no one could hear!

William recalled his later days. William growing up, yet a father who refused to listen to anything he said. For Larz Thomas only wanted to hear his own voice . . . his own words!

William Thomas came back to the present. His eyes were now staring out with calm decision. He went into the next room and called his father.

"What do you want?" roared Larz.

"I'd like to see you for a moment," said William.

"The fool won't keep me long," said Larz bitterly as he went to meet his son.

"We'll go upstairs," said William simply, and he marched up the stairs to the room that was sound-proof. Larz Thomas followed him blindly.

They went into the room and William closed the door. Then no one could hear what was happening . . . no one could hear the talk . . . or the screams!

Then William opened the door and walked out. Still no sound could be heard. For William was silent, and in his right hand he held Larz Thomas' bloody tongue!

CHILLY
CHAMBER MUSIC

SONGS FROM THE
SPOOK BOX!

ROW....ROW....ROW....YOUR BOAT
GENTLY DOWN THE STREAM!

ROW....ROW....ROW....YOUR BOAT
LAY YOUR HEAD DOWN TO DREAM!

ROW....ROW....ROW....YOUR BOAT
BETTER GET ON THE BEAM!

ROW....ROW....ROW....YOUR BOAT
LIFE IS BUT A SCREAM!!!

CHILLY
CHAMBER MUSIC

SONGS FROM THE
SPOOK BOX!

ALL ALONE...
I'M SO ALL ALONE!

ALL ALONE
BY THE TELEPHONE...

TRIED TO CALL...
BUT NOW I GROAN!!

DOESN'T MATTER 'CAUSE I'M
ALL ALONE!!

END OF THE LINE

3

I HEARD THE SCREAMS FROM THE OTHER END OF THE STATION, JOE. CAME AS FAST AS I COULD. I'LL GO DOWN AND TAKE A LOOK!

PROBABLY *DEAD*, SAM! I'LL GET THE DETAILS FROM THIS GUY HERE!

OKAY, MR. SUMMERS, I GOT YOUR NAME AND A COUPLE OF THE FACTS. GOOD THING FOR YOU I SAW THE ACCIDENT! BUT BE DOWN AT HEADQUARTERS TOMORROW MORNING FOR A FULL REPORT! NOW GET YOUR WIFE OUT OF HERE!

YES... YES! COME, CLARA... WE'RE GOING!

IT STARTED FROM *NOTHING--NOTHING!*

TRY TO FORGET ABOUT IT, CLARA! WE'LL FEEL BETTER ONCE WE'RE AT EMILY'S HOUSE!

CLARA! AFTER ALL THESE YEARS ...WHY, WHAT'S WRONG? YOU LOOK AS WHITE AS A SHEET!

OH, EMILY! WE...GEORGE AND I ... JUST WENT THROUGH A TERRIBLE ACCIDENT! OH, IT WAS *HORRIBLE!*

A MAN TRIED ...OH, I CAN'T EVEN TALK ABOUT IT!

TAKE IT EASY, CLARA.

I'LL GO INTO THE KITCHEN AND BREW A STRONG CUP OF COFFEE! THAT'LL CALM HER DOWN A LITTLE!

CLARA...MY HUSBAND'S NOT HOME YET. BUT...YOU CAN SEE WHAT HE LOOKS LIKE FROM HIS PICTURE BEHIND YOU! HE'S... OH, THERE'S THE PHONE!

BRRING G-G... BRRING!

G-GEORGE! T-THAT MAN--*THAT MAN!!*

T-THE *POLICE?!!* NO... *NO!!* OH, MY LORD ... *NOOOOO!!*

THE END

5